DATE DUE			

UNDERSTANDING
THROUGH
COMMUNICATION

UNDERSTANDING THROUGH COMMUNICATION

Structured Experiments in Self-Exploration

By

LOIS TIMMINS, Ed.D.

Director of Recreation Therapy
Timberlawn Psychiatric Hospital
Dallas, Texas

With a Foreword by

Howard M. Burkett, M.D.

Psychiatrist-in-Chief
Timberlawn Psychiatric Hospital
Dallas, Texas

CHARLES C THOMAS · PUBLISHER
Springfield · Illinois · U.S.A.

Published and Distributed Throughout the World by

CHARLES C THOMAS • PUBLISHER

BANNERSTONE HOUSE

301-327 East Lawrence Avenue, Springfield, Illinois, U.S.A.

© 1972, by CHARLES C THOMAS • PUBLISHER

ISBN 0-398-02430-8

Library of Congress Catalog Card Number 71-187680

With THOMAS BOOKS *careful attention is given to all details of manufacturing and design. It is the Publisher's desire to present books that are satisfactory as to their physical qualities and artistic possibilities and appropriate for their particular use.* THOMAS BOOKS *will be true to those laws of quality that assure a good name and good will.*

Printed in the United States of America

W-2

When men can freely communicate their thoughts and their sufferings, real or imaginary, their passions spend themselves in air, like gunpowder scattered upon the surface; but pent up by terrors, they work unseen, burst forth in a moment, and destroy everything in their course.

THOMAS ERSKINE
The Advantages of Free Speech
(Rex v. Paine, 1792)

FOREWORD

IT IS AN ESTABLISHED principle that in addition to constitutional or genetic factors, the milieu into which one is born determines to a large extent the nature of personality and behavior. The environment in which one is reared exerts constant influence, alters the emotions, and establishes the attitudes with which one deals with the experience he encounters in life.

Methods of communication between parents, siblings, peers, and other important figures are learned and adopted by the individual to be used for a lifetime of daily experiences and transactions with others. When faulty communication techniques are employed by these important figures or when the emotional environment is unhealthy and unacceptable, the child may choose not to communicate. When pathological mechanisms—especially denial and projection—are employed, they serve to further isolate the individual from meaningful interpersonal communication.

When indeed the cycle becomes so dominant that the individual relinquishes his contact with reality and becomes psychotic or when he uses a neurotic illness as a partial solution to an intolerable conflict, therapeutic intervention may be successful only when the patient is hospitalized. Hospitalization is the effective approach, principally because of the availability of external controls and therapeutic access to the patient via an active milieu program.

The evolution of the psychiatric hospital into a therapeutic community has been a relatively slow processs until recent years. After centuries of stagnation of psychiatric patients in custodial care, early in this century came the period of emphasis on treatment. The development of insulin treatment, electroconvulsive therapy, chemotherapy, and finally the phase of a therapeutic milieu have all occurred in the second third of this century. In its present phase, the psychiatric hospital has become a therapeutic instrument with heavy emphasis on the treatment of people with people.[1]

Timberlawn Psychiatric Hospital is a 152-bed, privately owned institution situated on eighteen acres of semi-wooded, landscaped ground on the eastern edge of the city of Dallas. Ninety-five percent of its patients are voluntary, and the remainder are hospitalized on civil commitment. All geographic areas of the North American continent are represented, and all diagnostic categories are accepted. However, patients with known organic brain disease, mentally retarded individuals, and those with narcotic addiction are not admitted except for diagnostic evaluation.

The physical plant consists of seven units, all segregated by sex except one 28 bed unit that houses both male and female patients.

The therapeutic emphasis in Timberlawn is psychotherapeutic, with both group experience and individual psychotherapy being available to every patient for whom these are clinically indicated.

The hospital is staffed by fifteen senior staff psychiatrists and five active consultants. It supports a three-year residency training program approved by the American Board of Psychiatry and Neurology. The school of Nursing of Baylor University utilizes the hospital for training its degree-program nurses in psychiatric hospital techniques. Other disciplines—social work, occupational therapy, recreation therapy, and psychology—use the hospital setting in their training programs.

Prior to 1957, there was occupational therapy, but no recreation therapy program. Dr. Lois Timmins joined the staff as Recreation Therapy Director in 1957. In that capacity, she has developed an extensive program that has become an integral part of the patient's therapeutic experience in Timberlawn. The Medical Staff has participated in the development of activity schedules that have become increasingly sophisticated and beneficial to the patients' therapeutic regime. A wide variety of activities, all subject to the approval of the activities therapist and the staff psychiarist, is available to the patient.

---

[1] Gralnick, Alexander (Ed.): *The Psychiatric Hospital as a Therapeutic Instrument*. New York, Brunner/Mazel, 1969.

It has become increasingly evident that the patient's experience in the Communication Class has been important and meaningful in his recovery. It is perhaps most evident that the Communication Class experience has been catalytic in psychotherapy, since therapists on the staff frequently report improved insights and self-awareness that facilitate psychotherapy.

It is also significant that long-discharged patients who return for follow-up care or those who are readmitted for hospitalization speak positively of their experience in Communication Class; indeed, in the latter instance, they often ask to be placed again in the Communication Class.

The author has the unique qualities of perceptiveness, directness, and objectivity, combined with a responsiveness and warmth that have made her a key figure in the recovery of many hospitalized patients. Her techniques are approved, and anyone who is engaged in teaching interpersonal communication would serve himself and his charges by a better understanding of her principles.

HOWARD M. BURKETT

PREFACE

THE DEVELOPMENT OF THE CONCEPT OF CLASS INSTRUCTION IN INTERPERSONAL COMMUNICATION

THE BASIC PURPOSE which has guided the development of a class in communication has been to assist psychiatric patients in establishing rewarding interpersonal relationships with their fellow human beings. Toward this end, I have combined the techniques of didactic, preceptive teaching with dynamically oriented group techniques.

During my first nine years as Director of Recreation Therapy at Timberlawn Psychiatric Hospital, I had observed more than seven thousand patients who were admitted to the hospital and ultimately discharged. Some patients had experienced life-long isolation and loneliness; others, though involved in complex social living, had enjoyed minimal warmth and empathy in their relationships. Many patients exhibited ignorance of the most simple precepts related to feelings and showed little awareness of emotions; moreover, they lacked vocabulary to express those emotions they recognized. They had no concept of self-change, nor did they know how or where to begin the process.

Subsequently, I developed a class which would teach such basic understandings to patients, including the course as a part of the activities program and calling it *Communication*.

At this writing, the Communication Class has been offered for four years; it meets three times a week and has an average attendance of between 30 and 35 persons. Some patients have participated in only a few sessions, while one patient attended 148. Included in this book are eighty-four lessons selected from approximately six hundred lessons taught to nearly a thousand participants. The methodology has been generic enough to meet the needs of vastly differing individuals and yet sufficiently

unthreatening to be utilized safely with a class of casually
screened patients.

Class experiments have been structured to examine effective
and ineffective responses to familiar situations in everyday life.
Instead of attempting to explore their deeper feelings and responses, participants have been led to look deeply at superficial
aspects of their living and to determine how these superficial
aspects are related to deeper problems. Direct confrontation of
the graver problems has not been undertaken. Self-relevation has
been no greater than patients have been willing to make in an
open class setting, nor have responses been sought that the
class instructor would be unable to help the patient work through
in class.

Verbal techniques have been emphasized throughout. Nonverbal communication has been examined occasionally but only
to demonstrate its inadequacy as contrasted with verbal techniques. Patients have been consistently urged to substitute verbal
for nonverbal methods of communication, even at the expense of
some sensory awareness.

In class experiments, all the appurtenances of everyday life
have been left intact and conventional modes of behavior carefully guarded. The classroom setting has been retained, with
participants sitting in chairs, not on the floor. Clothing con-
ventions have been observed, and techniques employing physical
contact scrupulously avoided.

APPRAISAL OF RESULTS

Many observations indicate that the class has been especially
effective in reaching depressed patients. The simple presentations
have helped such patients to be more assertive in their daily
relationships, thus providing a potential for some eventual relief
from their depression. Their immediate reactions to their first
honest communicative efforts, however, have been those of severe
anxiety and occasionally augmented depression, since they were
forced to confront the magnitude of their own aggressive feelings.

Those persons with marginal relatedness have exhibited very
slow and moderate changes in the direction of improved expres-

sion. Nevertheless, these patients have expressed gratitude for the satisfactions derived from participation in the simple communicative situations which the class offered.

The individuals with massive denial systems and rigid bipolar values also have exhibited a positive reaction to the class sessions. When challenged by aggressive group confrontations in the class setting, their immediate response has been anger and denial. The long-term effect of such confrontations on these patients, often considered recalcitrant in individual psychotherapy, has appeared to be increased insight.

The class has proved to be virtually valueless to patients with limited intelligence or to those suffering mental confusion during electroconvulsive therapy; therefore such patients are no longer assigned to the class. Patients expressing a high degree of thought fragmentation have been too disruptive for toleration by the group and are now placed in less expressive activities. Patients with high impulsive potential are admitted to the class, but frequently they are unwilling to accept the structure and discipline of the experiments and are dropped from the class upon their request.

ORGANIZATION OF THE BOOK

The book is divided into two parts: Book I represents eighty-four sessions organized into units. Book II presents theoretical material designed to help the reader understand the philosophy and methodology upon which the sessions have been based.

The sessions in Book I focus on problems which have long been recognized as trouble-producing. Each topic is approached from many angles, but the approach in any one session is not highly significant, nor is there any special significance in the order of the sessions. Clothing the sessions in many different outfits disguises the fact that the topics are related and may well create the illusion that the problems are more discrete than they actually are.

In the case of most sessions, the thesis topic is first presented in a brief lecture. This procedure serves to introduce the topic to those who were not present during the previous period, and it provides a warm-up for all members. The body of the session consists of structured experiments and practice drills created to develop and support the thesis.

Somewhere in the course of the session, a dilemma or paradox is posed to heighten awareness of the problem and starkly confront present inadequate responses or behavior. As the session proceeds, the participants take small and hopefully successful steps which lead to a progressive reconstruction of coping skills. The session concludes with a summary discussion.

The theoretical chapters, which treat the philosophy and methodology of the sessions, comprise Book II. Some readers will find reading of the theoretical chapters necessary for full understanding of the sessions. Others may encounter difficulty in understanding the theoretical chapters without referring to material included in the sessions. Therefore, movement back and forth from theory to session, according to the needs and background of the reader, is recommended.

A list of equipment and supplies needed for presentation of the entire series of sessions is included at the end of the book.

ACKNOWLEDGMENTS

I AM GRATEFUL to the founders and subsequent medical administrative officers of Timberlawn Psychiatric Hospital for creating an institutional tradition which fosters creative freedom in developing treatment modalities. I express special gratitude to Charles L. Bloss, M.D., formerly Medical Director, and to Howard M. Burkett, M.D., presently Psychiatrist-in-Chief, who has honored me by writing the Foreword. Specific mention should be made of the late William H. Wood, M.D., whose instruction was significant in the formulation of the ideas included in this book.

Further, I would like to thank specifically Timberlawn staff members Keith M. Johansen, M.D., Director of Activities Therapy, and Stanley L. Seaton, M.D., Director of the Day Hospital, for their valuable criticism and suggestions regarding the manuscript.

Finally, I should like to express deep gratitude to the hundreds of patients who have shared their ideas, feelings, and concerns during the conduct of the classes. The enthusiasm of the participants has provided my motivation to record the sessions and thereby make possible their use by others.

L.F.T.

CONTENTS

BOOK II
PHILOSOPHY AND METHODOLOGY

UNDERSTANDING
THROUGH
COMMUNICATION

BOOK I

STRUCTURED EXPERIMENTS IN SELF-EXPLORATION

Section I

Purposes and Problems of Communication

UNIT I—WHAT IS COMMUNICATION?

SESSION 1—THE IMPORTANCE OF LANGUAGE

The two greatest inventions of the human mind are writing and money—the common language of intelligence, and the common language of self-interest.

MARQUIS DE MIRABEAU[1]

Theoretical Presentation

Mᴀɴ's ᴀʙɪʟɪᴛʏ ᴛᴏ turn meaningless grunts into spoken words— and his spoken words into written symbols—probably represents his most important discovery. It has determined the development of most of those characteristics that differentiate him from other animals.

Communication embraces all the methods man employs in revealing ideas and information: speaking, writing, and signaling. It includes all means used to remain in touch with people separated by distance: television, radio, telephone, and telegraph. Communication also includes those ways that link the deceased with the living: books.

Through the use of language, both spoken and written, we experience commonality with other human beings. All social life, cooperative ventures, work, play, and politics depend upon the sharing of experiences through communication. Language makes possible the sharing of feelings with others, thus enabling the expression of relatedness and providing escape from loneliness. Language helps us to achieve self-knowledge: to polarize feelings, to discriminate between one feeling and another, to enjoy expressiveness, and to benefit from its catharsis.

NOTE: This session, which consists of lecture only, may be accompanied by discussion, a chalkboard exemplification of the concepts, and/or an actual illustration of one complete feeling interchange.

[1] Clodd, Edward: *The Story of the Alphabet*. London, George Newnes, 1900. Frontispiece.

A *satisfying feeling communication* may be viewed as a number of distinct procedures:

1. The sender obtains the attention of the person he wishes to talk to, indicating the reason he is communicating with him in particular instead of someone else. This initial step is an acknowledgement that it is unreasonable to expect a response from a person who is otherwise occupied or who is not aware that he is being addressed.
2. The receiver indicates that he is listening.
3. The sender states his message in language the receiver can understand, expressing personalized, self-generated feelings from a strictly self-contained point of view. He avoids projecting his feelings to others, reading the minds of others, expressing other's viewpoints, or attempting to express generalized feelings. He takes responsibility for the message he has sent.
4. The receiver may need to check the accuracy of his hearing of the message. After doing so, he acknowledges receipt of the message by a response which either expresses his own feelings or expresses empathetically how he would feel if he were the sender. The receiver's response has a profound effect upon the nature of subsequent communication on the part of the sender. Warm, responsive reactions encourage further communication. Apathetic, disinterested, vague responses discourage communication.
5. The sender responds with further expression of his feeling, an empathetic response to the feelings expressed by the receiver, or gratitude for the empathy the receiver has given him.

The following is an illustration of one complete feeling interchange between two people."

A Complete Feeling Communication

Sender: (Getting attention of Receiver) "Mildred, I want to talk with you about the car pool."
Receiver: (Acknowledging Sender) "O.K., Lucille. What about it?"

Sender: (Explaining why she is sending the message) "Charlie's car is in the garage today and he had to take my car." (Sending the message) "Can you drive my car pool this afternoon? I'm in a bind."

Receiver: (Acknowledging receipt of the message and expressing good-will) "Oh, gee, Lucille. I wish I could help you out." (Checking whether she has heard correctly) "You did say this afternoon, didn't you?"

(Responds, explaining her own feelings) "I feel bad about having to say no, because I've called on you twice in an emergency. I have an appointment to take Jennifer to the orthodontist." (Expressing empathy) "It really is a bind when you don't have a car."

Sender: (Acknowledging the acknowledgment) "Thanks for your concern. That helps me feel better, even if I still have the problem of the car pool."

(Expressing further personal feelings) "I feel awfully guilty when I can't carry my part of the load in the car pool." (When the feeling interchange is completed, suggesting action.) "If I took Jennifer to the orthodontist on the bus, would you be willing to do my car pool?"

Receiver: (Completing the negotiations for action) "Yes, that's a good idea. Jennifer likes to go with you anyway. That will be a good solution. Let's do it that way."

SESSION 2—TALK: THE GRAPHITE FOR PROBLEM SOLVING

Organization

Regular classroom seating. Members of the group form into pairs, sitting next to each other, and designate themselves as either No. 1 or No. 2.

Equipment

A timing device.

Instructions

"Both of you think about what you could do between 6:00 o'clock and 11:00 o'clock tonight, if you could do what you would enjoy most. No. 2's, you are to listen only and cannot talk. No. 1 person, talk to No. 2 person for four minutes about what you would most like to do with this time, what you would least like to do, and explain to your partner the why's of your choices."

Activity

No. 1's talk for the four minutes while No. 2's listen.

Instructions

"Now, No. 2's, recap what No. 1's said to you. You will have two minutes for the recap. No. 1's, you cannot talk during the recap."

Activity

During a timed two-minute period, No. 2's recap what No. 1's said while No. 1's listen.

Instructions

"No. 2 person, talk to No. 1 person for four minutes about what you would most like to do with the time this evening, what you would least like to do, and explain the why's of your choices to your partner. No. 1's, you cannot talk during this four minutes."

Activity

No. 2's talk for four minutes.

Instructions

"Now, No. 1's, you have two minutes to recap what No. 2's have said to you. Remember, No. 2's, you cannot talk during the recap."

Activity

No. 1's recap No. 2's statements during two minutes.

Instructions

"You will be together tonight from 6:00 o'clock to 11:00 o'clock. Discuss with each other how you will spend the time so that each of you will have the largest possible amount of what you want."

Activity

Partners have ten minutes to reach a joint decision on how to spend the evening. They remain seated together for the discussion which follows.

Questions for Discussion

1. Did you have difficulty in filling the four minutes when you yourself were talking?
2. How effectively did you express your true feelings concerning the ways you would like to spend the time?
3. When you were recapping, did you have difficulty in filling the two minutes?
4. Were you actually listening to what the other person said, as demonstrated by your ability to recap his ideas?
5. In your final joint decision, how much of what you wanted most to do would you get to do?
6. How much of what would be distasteful did you agree to do?
7. What means did you utilize to resolve differences?
8. Did you employ any tricks to avoid problems created by the difference between you? What tricks?

Response of the Pilot Group: Instructor's Observations

Most members of the group acknowledged that it was relatively easy to come to a joint decision after having spent the four minutes in expressive talk about their likes and dislikes. They acknowledged that they rarely used such a process before making a decision but that it would be helpful to talk more in advance of decision-making.

Many participants had difficulty talking for four minutes about their own interests, likes and dislikes. These persons discussed the reasons for their difficulty, since four minutes was actually a very short time to talk about one's interests. The instructor then pointed out that effective communication with a close peer may require many assaults on the same problem, spanning hours, weeks, months, and even years to accomplish a depth of understanding of another person's likes and dislikes.

Various members of the class reported using the following different tricks to avoid problems of difference:

1. They split the time, spending half the evening doing one person's enjoyable activities and the other half of the evening doing the other person's enjoyable activities. This compromise avoided any real confrontation of differences.
2. They included all that each person wanted, avoiding any real confrontation of differences and any necessity for making choices.
3. They avoided the activities suggested by either of them as being most enjoyable, and met on a common ground not related to what either really wanted to do. Thus, neither of the two parties was able to participate in the activity most enjoyable to him. In order to achieve a common activity, both abnegated their true interests.

SESSION 3—A LISTENER WHO HEARS

Organization

Members of the group are seated in a circle or in concentric circles.

Equipment

None.

Instructions

"Will someone volunteer to demonstrate our procedure for today? (Someone volunteers. He remains seated.) We will call you the Sender. Sender, select another member of the group to whom you would like to talk about something you feel. (He selects someone, who also remains in his seat.) We will call you the Receiver. Now, Sender, talk to the Receiver about your feelings on some subject. You will say what you have to say in front of the class. Be reasonably brief. (The Sender talks about his feelings.) Receiver, try to recapitulate what the Sender has said to you. Feed back to him what he has said. You are to express his feelings, not yours. Do not respond with your own feelings; merely repeat what he has said. You may shorten it somewhat or summarize if you wish, but you are not to alter the meaning of what has been said or interject your own feelings or give any response. (Receiver attempts to recapitulate what the Sender has said.) Sender, are you satisfied with the recapitulation? I am asking you to decide whether you feel you have been clearly understood. (Sender makes his decision.) If the Sender states that his feelings have been accurately recounted, the Receiver will earn the right to be the next Sender. If the Sender is dissatisfied with the recapitulation, the Receiver loses his right, and we will then ask for another volunteer to be the Sender and select another Receiver. In other words, you earn the right to be a Sender and to talk by listening well."

Activity

Participants proceed as above until about ten minutes before the closing of the period. The last ten minutes are devoted to discussion of the difficulties involved in listening carefully to what others say.

SESSION 4—SENDING AND RECEIVING: BALL THROWING

Prior Preparation Required

In advance of the session, one member of the class is selected and given secret instructions as to his forthcoming role. He will be assigned to sit in the chair at the front of the room. Another class member will throw balls to him. Unless the thrower gives him specific instructions the catcher is to respond capriciously, so that it is impossible for the thrower to predict his actions.

Organization

Regular classroom seating, except that a space is cleared at the front of the room. A chair, placed at one side, faces the center of this space.

Equipment

A number of balls of varying sizes and weights, including, if possible, one rather heavy ball (e.g. a billiard ball) which will make a loud, startling crash when it drops to the floor.

Theoretical Presentation

Many of us get into communication trouble because we answer questions before we ask them. We try to be, at the same time, both the sender and the receiver of a message.

We say, "I know you probably won't want to, but would you like to go to the movies tonight?"

"I know you are watching the football game, and won't want to do it, but would you mind going out and turning off the hose on the lawn?"

"I know just how you feel about this, but I'll ask you anyway."

Does this kind of talk sound familiar?

Instructions

"Which of you know that you have a tendency to do this? You are the ones we will need to participate in our exercise

---

NOTE: This exercise is a graphically concrete presentation of an important concept. The success of the exercise depends upon the equipment selected, the protagonists involved, and on the ability of the instructor to enliven the dramatic quality of the interchanges. Prior preparation is required.

today. Someone who raised his hand, volunteer to come to the front. (A volunteer comes to the front.) You will stand here, about ten feet from the person assigned to sit in the chair. Chairsitter, please take your place. Now, here are a number of balls. You will notice that they are of different sizes and weights, some small, some large, some light and some heavy. Throw the balls to our catcher in such a way that he can catch them."

Activity

The volunteer throws the balls to the assistant, who catches some and allows others to drop. The exercise may be repeated several times with several throwers.

Instructions

"These balls represent communicative messages. Some messages are light, some are heavy, some are large and important, some are inconsequential. What conclusions about communication have the balls demonstrated?"

Activity

A discussion is held concerning the process of communication based on the points inherent in the ball-throwing session.

Response of the Pilot Group

Instructor's Observations

As the exercise proceeded, the thrower became increasingly frustrated when the catcher did not catch the balls. The thrower first berated himself for not being a good thrower. Then, he became annoyed with the catcher. Finally, he realized that it was possible to communicate with the catcher before throwing the ball, apprising him of the size and weight of the ball, and the timing and direction of the throw. Despite this communication, he realized that he could not control the behavior of the catcher once the ball had left his hand.

Summary of Discussion

It is not possible to be the sender *and* the receiver of a communication unless you are talking to yourself.

It is helpful to get the attention of the receiver before talking, and apprise him of the fact that you are going to send a message.

If you indicate to the receiver that it would please you if he heard the message, he is more likely to try to hear it.

It is helpful to describe the nature and importance of the message before sending it. "I want to talk to you about . . . It is of great importance to me because . . ."

Once the message leaves your mouth, it is no longer possible to have any control over the reception. Hence the maxim: "Think before you speak."

SESSION 5—SUMMARY: COMMUNICATION, THE BALSAM FOR FRUSTRATION

. . . communication is a balsam which heals the wounds acquired in the battle for life.[2]

Theoretical Presentation

A balsam is a balm or soothing agent. The word derives from the ancient practice of utilizing the exudations from certain trees as ointments for medicinal use.

Communication can be a balsam for frustration, soothing the wounds of hurt and loss, thus dissipating anxiety and loneliness.

Organization

Regular classroom seating.

Equipment

Chalkboard and chalk.

Instructions

"Let's talk first about situations in which communication is easy and when frustration is minimal. I will write the points on the board as you suggest them. When is communication easy?"

Activity

The instructor itemizes on the board the situations suggested by class members.

Instructions

"Now let's consider situations when communication is difficult. If we can discover ways of facilitating communication when it is difficult, we may find some clues as to how we can use communication as a balsam for frustration."

Activity

The instructor itemizes on the board the difficult and easy situations suggested by class members. Following this step, he summarizes conclusions on the basis of suggestions made by class participants.

---

[2] Ruesch, Jurgen, and Bateson, Gregory: *Communication: The Social Matrix of Psychiatry.* New York, Norton, 1951, p. 92.

Response of the Pilot Group: Collation

Communication is easy . . .

When you have a common ground.

When you communicate in short bits.

When the problem is not too severe.

When you have no stake in either a negative or an affirmative response.

When you feel warm toward the other person.

When time is not limited.

When the other person appears interested and listens attentively.

When you get a lot of positive feedback.

When the other person is empathetic.

Communication is difficult . . .

When you don't know anything about the subject.

When talking about very personal subjects.

When you have decided not to discuss the subject.

When you are afraid of communicating something you don't want the other person to know.

When you are afraid of rejection, rebuff, or a sharp or impatient answer.

After a nonverbal outburst or physical attack.

When the emotion is very strong and overpowering or violent.

When one person feels separated from another.

When communicating with a stranger.

When you talk with others who do not communicate well or who talk without letting you get in a word.

When you know that people are not interested in the subject you are talking about.

When the other person appears disinterested, gives no answer, or puts periods on the conversation.

When people are amused and you did not intend to be funny, or when laughter is not called for.

To use communication as a balsam for frustration . . .

Use verbal communication instead of nonverbal outbursts and physical attacks.

Communicate on common ground about subjects of mutual knowledge and concern.

Practice communication on problems which are not too severe and emotions that are not too violent or overpowering.

Practice communication with people toward whom you feel friendly, and who give warm, empathetic feedback.

Talk about big problems a bit at a time.

Work on difficult problems when time is not limited.

Help others to communicate by listening carefully, giving feedback, and responding empathetically.

Do not laugh at the problems of others except when they present them as funny.

UNIT II—WHEN WORDS ARE ABSENT

SESSION 1—NONVERBAL COMMUNICATION

Prior Preparation Required

DURING THE PRECEDING class period, each participant was asked to determine some type of help he would like from another member in the group. The participant was also told to bring to the class any materials which might be involved in obtaining the help needed.

Theoretical Presentation

Should we consider as language only that form of communication of thought which is produced by the vocal organs, then transmitted by air waves and received by the human ear? Or should the term *language* be extended to anything that serves the purpose of transferring meaning so as to include first and foremost, writing; secondly, meaningful gesture; lastly, the numerous symbolic systems that embrace the drumbeats of the African natives, the smoke signals of of the American Indians, the knotted ropes of the Incas, the notched twigs of certain Australian tribes, as well as fully modern devices such as traffic lights, semaphores, and even directional signs, like the arrows that mark a one-way street?[1]

Nonverbal communication takes many forms and constitutes the largest portion of all communication, whereas verbal communication represents only a small portion of interpersonal communication.

Nonverbal communication may be physiological and involuntary. Intimate feelings are exposed by blushing, perspiring, blanching, or trembling.

Verbal messages are augmented or countermanded by voluntary actions such as smiles, frowns, the lift of an eyebrow, or a wink.

NOTE: This session requires prior preparation.

[1] Pei, Mario: *Language for Everybody, What It is and How to Master It.* New York, Pocket Books, 1958, p. 21.

Gestures may express feelings of aggressive attack with a threatening fist or a shaking finger. Hands-in-pockets may mean quiet relaxation or repressive withholding of a threatening attack. Many such gestures have survived throughout many centuries and in many cultures. The thumbs-down gesture (*police verso*) was the ancient Roman symbol used by spectators to condemn a vanquished gladiator to death. As a derogatory gesture, it survives today.

Bodily postures and positions convey messages. Bodily vigor suggests a forceful, energetic attack on a situation or problem; slumping conveys apathy. Bodily postures of lassitude or languor convey indifference or extreme withdrawal.

Clothes, houses, automobiles, and other material possessions speak nonverbally of affluence or poverty, conformity, or non-conformity. Native costumes symbolize concepts and values within a culture as well as differences between cultures. Symbols convey status and power.

Processions and parades communicate secret ideas, religious concepts and political ideologies. So do the accompanying display of symbols, in rituals such as the burning of sacred fires or incense, and the sacrifice of money, time, or lives in behalf of a cause.

Pictographic language in cartoons, posters, and road signs conveys messages which cross cultural and language barriers.

In mass spectacles, verbal communication cannot be effective, and signals are used instead. The referee in sports has special gestural signals for each foul or violation, and any one of the thousands of spectators may understand the language. The policeman directs the traffic by means of signals. Anyone who has travelled in a foreign country encounters the need to learn a new signal language even if he is conversant with the spoken language.

Gestural language may become necessary because verbal communication is not possible. In scuba diving, the guide asks each underwater diver if he is okay by using the thumb and first-finger circle accompanied by a questioning look. The diver answers okay with the same gesture given in an assertive movement plus a nod of the head to confirm the gesture. If he is out of air, he draws his index finger across his throat and points up to indicate he is going to surface. Similar gesture languages have been developed for almost every trade and sport.

Noises without words are highly communicative. The single notable comment ascribed to the psychiatrist, "Mmmmmmm . . .," may be said in a hundred different ways to mean a hundred different things.

In our class today, we will experiment with the use of non-verbal communication. Later we will discuss how this communication differs from that requiring words.

Organization
Regular classroom seating.

Equipment
Masking tape; each participant's equipment as required for his project.

Instructions
"For homework, you were asked to bring materials related to a project on which you wanted some help. If you did not bring your materials which are necessary, you cannot participate in the exercise.

"Without using language of any kind, you are to approach some other member of the group and ask for the help you need with your project. You cannot speak at all. Do not speak or write. Try to get the help you need and accomplish the task you have in mind.

"If you feel that you will be unable to refrain from speaking during the exercise, you may use the masking tape to seal your mouth."

Activity
Participants attempt to accomplish the cooperative task without talking. When the activity has subsided, the instructor conducts a discussion.

Questions for Discussion
1. What means did you use to convey the message about the kind of help you needed?

2. Was it easier or harder than by using words? What part of it was easier? What part harder?
3. Were there certain kinds of topics easier to convey nonverbally than other topics? What kinds of topics were the most difficult? Why?
4. In what ways is nonverbal communication most different from verbal communication?

Response of the Pilot Group

Instructor's Observations

All members of the group rejected use of masking tape to cover their mouths. The suggestion brought a response of revulsion. Even those who were usually silent during discussion periods—and who rarely opened their mouths anyway—pleaded that they would be able to keep their mouths shut without the tape.

The following communicative projects were selected:

1. How to roll up another person's hair.
2. How to play a game of dominoes.
3. How to finish the edges of an embroidered towel.
4. How to play clock solitaire.
5. How to be a writer.
6. How to chord some original music.
7. How to solve a crossword puzzle.
8. How to put together an incorrectly cut dress.

Summary of Discussion

Nonverbal communication functions best in the realm of the tangible.

It is difficult to establish place and time without words.

It is difficult or virtually impossible to express abstract ideas nonverbally.

Without words, it is more difficult to express emotions than it is to give instructions.

Nonverbal expression creates cumulative frustration.

Nonverbal messages are especially subject to receptor distortion.

SESSION 2—MOVEMENT TO AUGMENT WORDS: MASS DOUBLING

Organization

Members of the group are instructed to form into pairs, and to designate one person in each pair as No. 1 and one person as No. 2.

Equipment

None.

Instructions

"No. 1's are to move around in the room and talk with other No. 1's on any subject you choose. Each No. 2 is to follow along just behind his own No. 1 and imitate or *double* his bodily movements as he talks. No. 2's are to remain slightly behind No. 1's and are not to talk at all, either to their own No. 1, to other No. 1's or to any other No. 2's. If No. 1's become annoyed with their No. 2's, they can scold them, tell them to go away, or express whatever feelings they have. No. 2's are not to respond with talking, nor are they to go away when sent away, but are to remain just behind No. 1's at all times."

Activity

Members of the class wander about the room as instructed.

Instructions

"Now we will reverse roles. No. 2's will talk with other No. 2's while No. 1's follow them and *double* all their bodily movements. If No. 2's become annoyed with their No. 1's, they can scold them, tell them to go away or express whatever they feel. No. 1's are not to respond with talking nor are they to go away when sent away, but are to remain with No. 2's."

Activity

Members of the class proceed as before. The leader then conducts a discussion of responses to the exercise.

Response of the Pilot Group: Quotations from Participants

"We found it extremely difficult not to talk. We weren't able to confine our activities to the movements of the one we were doubling."

"We became aware of the importance of bodily movements when a person is talking."

"We became so self-conscious about bodily activity that verbal communication was almost impossible."

"The nonverbal message may agree with the verbal message or it may contradict it. It may clarify the verbal message or it may interfere with and confuse it."

SESSION 3—IDEAS WITHOUT WORDS: PICTOGRAPHS

Organization
Members of the class are seated at tables.

Equipment
One piece of scratchboard for each participant; one 3-in. brad or nail or other stylus for each participant.

Instructions
"Imagine that you are living today in your own home situation, with your family, and with your present belongings. However, there is to be one major difference. Language-wise, the situation is as it was 6,000 years ago, before the invention of written language. For some reason, you will not be home when your husband or wife returns this evening. You will need to leave your spouse a note explaining where you are and when you will return. This note is to be scratched on a rock tablet and left for your spouse. The piece of scratchboard represents the rock tablet, and the nail is your only available stylus. You cannot use any words."

Activity
Class members work individually to write the notes on the scratchboards, using pictography. When they have completed the notes, the instructor continues.

Instructions
"Let us now imagine that a natural disaster completely obliterates all human life in your area. Six thousand years pass. Some archaeologists come to excavate your town and discover your rock tablet.

"Take your scratchboards and hide them face down somewhere in the room, so that the tablets are completely shuffled and all identity of the writer is completely obliterated."

Activity
Members of the class hide their rock tablets.

Instructions

"Now imagine that you are one of the archaeologists. You excavate the site, and you find one of these rock tablets. Go and find a tablet."

Activity

Members of the class move around the room and pick up someone else's scratchboard.

Instructions

"Study the message on the rock tablet you have discovered. Decipher the message and report it to us. Also, tell us what you know about the civilization, culture, life, and personality of the writer."

Activity

Each member of the class, in turn, attempts to decipher the message on the rock tablet he has found. No feedback is allowed from the person who wrote it, since he supposedly died 6,000 years ago.

Instructions

"Now let's talk about the kind of experiences you had in attempting to decipher the rock tablets. What did you notice about the communicative process when it involves no language?"

Activity

The class members participate in the discussion while the instructor writes the salient points on the chalkboard.

Instructions

"Without a written language it would be hard to communicate most of the aspects of our living today. Let me read you a quotation."

We have only to assume the absence of any medium whereby we could communicate with friends at a distance, or whereby the now complex and countless dealings between man and man could be set down and every transaction thus "brought to book," to realize the hopeless tangle of our social life. All that memory failed to overlap would be an absolute blank; the dateless and otherwise uninscribed monuments which the past had left behind would but deepen the darkness; all knowledge of the strivings and speculations of men of old would have been unattainable; all observation and experience through which science has advanced from guesses to certainties irretrievably lost; life could have been lived only from "hand to mouth," and the spectacle presented of an arrested world of sentient beings. Save in fragmentary echoes repeated by fugitive bards, the great epics of East and West would have perished, and the immortal literature of successive ages never have existed. The invention of writing alone made possible the passage from barbarism to civilization, and secured the continuous progress of the human race.[2]

Activity

At the conclusion of the reading, the class is dismissed without further comment.

Response of the Pilot Group

Quotations from Participants

"I noticed that the need to communicate existed even when the medium was difficult."

"I thought it would be easy to do, but it turned out to be very hard."

"Pictographic communication is effective only when you know the person who wrote it. The spouse would possibly have been able to understand the note, but one who did not know the particular people involved would not have been able to understand much."

"We imagined our own life situation and read ourselves into the reading of the other's tablets."

"It is effective when it is done by someone who has a facility with symbols. Some members of the class were quite good at drawing and could make themselves clear. I can't draw and I couldn't say anything anyone could understand."

Instructor's Summary

Some of the pictographs we used in class today are similar to ones used in tablets written thousands of years ago. The sun

---

[2] Clodd, *op. cit.*, p. 13.

to symbolize day and the moon to symbolize night are examples of such universal symbols.

Pictographic communication is vague and nonspecific.
Language makes accurate, effective communication possible.

UNIT III—WHEN COMMUNICATION IS ABSENT

SESSION 1—SILENCE: THE SACK

Prior Preparation Required

BEFORE ANY MEMBER of the class enters the room, a staff member, an outsider, or another participant puts on the sack and takes a place in the classroom, either sitting or lying. The person in the sack is instructed not to speak nor make any kind of noise. He can respond only in a nonverbal manner within the sack. He is not to reveal his identity.

Organization

Regular classroom seating.

Equipment

A sack large enough to cover a human being. It may be helpful if the person inside can see out, but those outside must not be able to see in.

Instructions

The instructor starts the class and begins a lecture on some aspect of communication, as if The Sack were not present. He continues the lecture until group agitation becomes directed toward The Sack. When this occurs, the instructor reacts as though he had no previous knowledge of The Sack, professing ignorance of its purpose and how it got there.

Activity

At this point, members of the group are allowed to deal with The Sack in whatever way they choose, short of making a

---

NOTE: This session involves preparation of the sack in advance, as well as the selection of the person to be in the sack when the session begins. The lesson spans two sessions.

physical attack that might injure the person in the sack. Confrontation of The Sack is allowed to go on until it is exhausted or until about ten minutes are left for discussion. The rest of the period and all of the following period are devoted to discussion of the experience of The Sack: the experience of non-communication and responses to it.

Questions for Discussion

1. What were your responses to The Sack?
2. What did you not know about The Sack?
3. What did you feel like doing about The Sack? When someone else will not communicate with you, what do you feel like doing?
4. How many of you liked The Sack? How many had no feeling? How many disliked The Sack? What other feelings did you have?

Response of the Pilot Group

Quotations from Participants

"I felt The Sack was a challenge. I was aggravated when I could not unsack it. I was pleased with my initiative in trying to unsack The Sack. It was the first aggressive thing I ever did in my life."

"I felt we should have made an effort to communicate with The Sack and Sack should have made an effort to communicate with us."

"I felt The Sack did not deserve any help. I felt no interest in The Sack because it had nothing to give me."

"I was afraid of The Sack. Nothing could have induced me to communicate with it. It was ugly, repulsive, antagonistic. I was delighted when it hit its head against the wall."

"The Sack gave me a feeling of isolation and claustrophobia. I thought The Sack's object was to protect its feelings."

"I felt The Sack wanted to remain anonymous. That was his business. We interpreted the lack of communication as antagonism."

"I had no feeling. I felt The Sack was an *it* rather than a person. I was curious that it was alive."

"We did not know his purpose, his reactions, his identity; whether he was alone or part of a conspiracy; whether he was vulnerable; how to communicate with him; how to help him; or even whether he wanted help."

"I assumed the leader would do something about The Sack eventually."

"I thought The Sack was a test of impulsiveness, so I didn't respond."

"I thought The Sack was to show that you can't depend on the other person to communicate."

"I hoped no one would respond, so the Leader's idea wouldn't work and we could get even with her."

Instructor's Observations

Results of the poll of the class and their responses to The Sack were as follows:

Actively liked The Sack	6
No feeling	4
Empathy	10
Curiosity	16
Dislike	2
Fear	1

The group became increasingly agitated as the period progressed. Various members tried to communicate with The Sack, but The Sack would not answer. One participant went to The Sack, poked it and tried to remove the sack. Other participants objected, saying that no one had a right to take the sack off if the person inside it did not want it taken off.

Some members expressed a desire to get on with the class, and said that it was unreasonable to have The Sack take the whole period when we should be talking about communication. Others of the group continued to attempt to ignore The Sack, but found it impossible.

Instructor's Summary

If we do not communicate, we have no chance whatsoever of meeting our own needs. Uncommunicative behavior produces very little active liking in other people.

SESSION 2—NO EARS TO HEAR: DEAFNESS

Organization
Participants move freely about the room to form random pairs.

Equipment
Cards picturing the sign language of the deaf, obtainable free from the local association for the deaf.

Instructions
"I will give each of you a card showing the sign language of the deaf. Today you are all to be deaf. Move around the room. Find five different people, and ask one question of each person. Do not talk aloud. Use deaf language only. Make no sounds. Answer questions asked of you, but in deaf language also."

Activity
Participants move around the room, carrying out the instructions. When the activity has subsided and each person in the room has asked and been asked the five questions, the leader asks members of the group to return to their original seats. A discussion follows, with important points written on the chalkboard.

Response of the Pilot Group: Quotations from Participants
"The limitation made me impatient to get along with the message."

"I enjoyed it. It gave me an excuse to be more demonstrative than usual."

"I felt a lack of emphasis."

"I used verbal communication for confirmation of the message."

"I was preoccupied with my own message."

"I felt a closeness when both people were handicapped as to the method of communication. The mutual handicap equalized the relationship."

"It was necessary to simplify the message."

"People paid more attention than they usually do."

"It was frustrating. You had to repeat the message."

"Facial expressions became more important when it was not possible to use words."

SESSION 3—NO VOICE TO SPEAK: MUTENESS

Organization

Regular classroom seating.

Equipment

A hood made out of cloth, large enough to fit over the head and having slits for the eyes. The hood hides all facial expression.

Instructions

"I would like for some of you—one at a time—to come to the front and attempt to communicate without the use of sound or words. You will be asked to put on this hood so that members of the class cannot observe your facial expressions. You will try to communicate some message to the group or to an individual in the group, but you will have to communicate this message without any words or sounds. You can use body movements only. Is there someone who will be first?"

Activity

One member of the group comes forward, puts on the hood, and attempts to communicate without the use of sound or words.

Instructions

"Now, class, tell me what he said."

Activity

Members of the class attempt to interpret his message. The instructor then asks the person at the front what he intended to convey.

Each volunteer proceeds in a similar routine.

After a number of persons have participated, the leader conducts a discussion of the experiences involved, writing salient points on the chalkboard.

Response of the Pilot Group: Quotations from Participants

"There seems to be some relationship between happiness and energy and sadness and lack of energy. This is not always so, however, since sometimes happiness is expressed through lack of movement.

"Movement is related to emotion, but it is sometimes difficult to tell which emotion is meant by which movement."

"Through movement, it is difficult to express specific ideas or degrees of feeling."

"Hands are the most obvious parts of bodily movement expression."

"People differ in their abilities to express ideas or feelings through bodily movement."

"Some people found it difficult not to talk while wearing the hood."

"My sense of identity must be related to having my face out in the open and having people see my expression. I felt a loss of identity when I was wearing the hood."

Section II

Emotions from A to Z

UNIT I–EXPRESSION OF FEELINGS

SESSION 1–VOCABULARY RETRIEVAL

Theoretical Presentation

No scientist is able to develop a theory without an adequate nomenclature to support his method and conclusions. A wide vocabulary of words that describe feelings makes possible a process of self-study.

To be expressive, it is necessary to delineate and define behavior by distinguishing one feeling from another in words which express pertinent differences. A differential vocabulary with which to express feelings can increase an awareness of feelings and enrich emotional living through extending the range of emotions felt.

On the contrary, the ability to be aware of feelings and to express feelings is inordinately hampered by insufficient vocabulary and lack of knowledge as to the exact meaning of the words used.

The attempt to master a language of feelings is a prodigious task. Feelings occupy every hour of our lives, leaping from dream to wakefulness, from imagination to reality, outward into action and inward to cause somatic pain and distress. We are searching for a nomenclature to describe an ephemeral, fleeting phenomena in constant flux; one feeling commingles with another, transforming almost before recognition. Other feelings burrow into the unconscious to disappear from observation altogether.

In the search for a description of feelings, man becomes entangled in his own circumvention. Man can transform his feelings when he does not wish to acknowledge or recognize them. When we are afraid, instead of feeling fear, we may feel a gnawing in the stomach. When we are angry, we may develop neuromuscular hypertension and a tension headache. Happiness and contentment may be experienced as productivity on the job or an increased satisfaction in sorting out debris in closets or garage.

In the area of feelings, we further expand the process of self-deception by transformation of the vocabulary itself through the use of the euphemism. If we change the word, we believe that we somehow can transform a feeling which is unpleasant or guilt-producing into one which is pleasant—or at least less unpleasant—and consequently free ourselves from some of the guilt related to the feeling. We think it is better to be annoyed than angry. We think it is better to be upset than afraid. We think it is better to be nervous than helpless or lonely.

Despite these numerous complications, we can increase our ability to recognize and communicate feelings if we can increase our vocabulary. Today and for the next few sessions we will be examining the words we have available to express our feelings.

Can you distinguish annoyance from rage? Can you distinguish joy from elation? Can you distinguish spite from disgust?

Organization

Regular classroom seating. Participants will be split into groups of six to ten, seated around tables.

Equipment

Lined paper and pencil for each participant, additional paper, rubber cement, one pair of scissors for each group.

Instructions

"Write your name in the top right-hand corner of your paper. Divide your paper into two columns. Now, make a list of every feeling you have ever had. Skip a line between each feeling you write."

Activity

Members of the group list their feelings. When they have ceased writing, the activity proceeds.

Instructions

"Now get together into groups of six to ten persons, each group around a table.

"Cut each paper in half. Then, cut each word separately, cutting on the line between the words. Alphabetize altogether the words from the members of your group. When the words are alphabetized, paste them onto sheets of paper to make a list in alphabetical order."

Activity

Members of the class follow the instructions.

Instructions

"A member of Group 1 will read its list of words beginning with A. Other groups, look at your lists and insert any words you do not have. If you have other words not on Group 1's list, tell us what they are. Each group should add any words it does not have, so that every group will end up with a composite list."

Activity

Groups follow the instructions with the words beginning with A.

Instructions

"Group 2, read the list of words beginning with B."

Activity

Groups augment their list of words beginning with B. The activity continues, with each group in turn reading words which begin with a consecutive letter. An additional session may be required to complete the lists.

All groups should ultimately have the same list of words. If the raw lists are in fairly good order, they can be used for succeeding lessons. If not, one complete set of words can be typed double-spaced and mimeographed for use by each member in the following lessons.

Response of the Pilot Group

Instructor's Summary

The repetition of many words enabled class members to recognize that people experience approximately the same feelings, and that their own emotions were neither unique nor unusual. The list provided a reassuring commonality.

Vocabulary List Produced

Abandonment
Abasement
Adequacy
Adjustment
Adoration
Affection
Age
Aggravation
Alarm
Aliveness
Aloofness
Ambition
Ambivalence
Anger
Animosity
Anxiety
Apathy
Appreciation
Apprehension
Assurance
Attractiveness
Awareness
Awe
Belonging
Benevolence
Betrayal
Bewilderment
Bias
Bitterness
Blessedness
Bliss
Boredom
Boundlessness
Capability
Caring
Childishness
Closeness
Coldness
Comfort
Compassion
Competitiveness
Comradeship
Concern
Confidence

Confinement
Confusion
Consolation
Contempt
Contentment
Control
Conviviality
Curiosity
Deadness
Defeat
Dejection
Delight
Dependency
Depression
Desertion
Desire
Desolation
Despair
Desperation
Detachment
Devotion
Discomfort
Discouragement
Disgust
Dishonor
Disillusionment
Disorganization
Dissatisfaction
Distrust
Dizziness
Doubt
Dread
Ease
Ecstasy
Embarrassment
Empathy
Emptiness
Energy
Enthusiasm
Envy
Esteem
Euphoria
Exaltation
Exhaustion

Exhilaration
Exuberance
Expectancy
Failure
Fatigue
Fear
Fidelity
Flippancy
Forgiveness
Freedom
Friendliness
Fright
Frivolity
Frustration
Futility
Generosity
Gladness
Goodness
Grandiosity
Gratification
Greed
Grief
Grossness
Guilt
Happiness
Hate
Helplessness
Honor
Hopelessness
Hostility
Humiliation
Humility
Hunger
Hurt
Illness
Impatience
Inadequacy
Independence
Indifference
Inferiority
Innocence
Insecurity
Intimacy
Irritation

Isolation
Jealousy
Joy
Lethargy
Liking
Limitation
Loneliness
Longing
Love
Loyalty
Maladjustment
Malaise
Melancholy
Misery
Morbidity
Naivete
Nausea
Nearness
Nervousness
Nostalgia
Nothingness
Oppression
Optimism
Pain
Panic
Paranoia
Passion
Patience
Peace
Pensiveness
Persecution
Pessimism
Pity
Pleasure
Possessiveness
Prayerfulness
Preparedness
Pride
Protectedness
Protectiveness
Purposelessness
Puzzlement
Rebelliousness
Regret

Rejection
Relaxation
Reluctance
Remorse
Repression
Resentment
Respect
Revenge
Revulsion
Sadness
Safety
Satiety
Satisfaction
Self-awareness
Self-centeredness
Self-consciousness
Self-containment
Self-destructiveness
Selfishness

Self-recrimination
Serenity
Shame
Shyness
Sickness
Sincerity
Sleepiness
Smothering
Solitude
Somberness
Spite
Spontaneity
Stability
Stinginess
Strength
Stress
Subserviency
Superiority
Surprise

Suspicion
Sympathy
Tenderness
Terror
Thankfulness
Thirst
Timidity
Tingling
Tiredness
Togetherness
Tolerance
Tranquility
Trust
Ugliness
Unattractiveness
Unawareness
Unconcern
Understanding
Uneasiness

Unimportance
Unity
Unpreparedness
Unworthiness
Urgency
Usefulness
Uselessness
Volubility
Vulnerability
Wakefulness
Warmth
Weariness
Well-being
Wistfulness
Wonderment
Worry
Worthlessness
Worthiness

SESSION 2—CLASSIFYING THE VOCABULARY

Organization

Participants keep their same groups of six to ten formed at the previous session; they are seated around tables.

Equipment

Lists of feelings compiled by the groups in the previous session; chalkboard and chalk, pencil and paper for each group.

Instructions

"Examine your lists. What are the major categories of feelings?"

Activity

Members of the class suggest major categories, and the instructor writes them on the board.

Instructions

"Working in your groups, try to classify the feelings on your list into the categories we have established. Write the major categories on the top of the blank sheets. Go through the composite list, and try to decide which category each word should be in. On each sheet, write the words which belong in that category."

Activity

Members of the class work as long as necessary on the classification of words.

Questions for Discussion

1. What difficulties did you encounter in your attempts to classify the words?
2. Were there certain feelings which were impossible to classify?

Activity

Each group is asked to give a report of their discussion. Major ideas suggested in the reports are written on the chalkboard.

Response of the Pilot Group: Summary of Discussion

Some feelings are directed toward the self and have no relation to other people; some are directed toward other people.

Some feelings are generalized and some are very specific.

Some feelings are physical.

Some feelings are related to values that we have been taught are good or bad, right or wrong.

Some feelings express a desire for action—like the urge to hit someone.

Some feelings express the absence of something—like apathy or boredom.

Some feelings we think of as positive and others we think of as negative.

Some feelings are aggressive and some are passive.

Some feelings express isolation and some express sociability.

Some feelings are constructive and other feelings are destructive.

Some feelings draw you toward others and other feelings push you away from others.

SESSION 3—WORDS TO EXPRESS THE SELF

Organization

Regular classroom seating.

Equipment

Pencil and paper for each participant, one dictionary for each group.

Instructions

"Write your name in the upper right-hand corner of your paper. Now, think about some recent situation in which you were angry. When was it? Who was involved? Was action involved? Where did the action take place? Select the feeling word that most accurately describes your feeling in that particular situation. Write that word on your paper. Then, look up the word in the dictionary and write down the definition. Is this the word which accurately describes your feeling in the situation referred to? If not, select another word. Look it up. Continue this process until you find a word which describes how you felt. Members of the group may give assistance to anyone who has difficulty finding a suitable word to fit his feeling."

Activity

Participants follow the exercise. When they have finished, the instructor conducts a discussion about the words which were selected.

Questions for Discussion

1. Could you find a word which clearly describes your feeling?
2. Is the word generalized or specific?
3. Does the word have a value? Is it good or bad, right or wrong? If it has a value, can you find another word for the same feeling which does not have a value?
4. What word describes the same feeling in a lesser intensity? The same feeling in a greater intensity?
5. If the feeling arose in a different situation, would the same word adequately describe the feeling?
6. Would the most suitable word to describe the feeling be the

same if the feeling occurred long ago rather than ten minutes ago?

7. Is the word suitable when it describes a feeling you have toward someone else as well as a feeling someone else has toward you? Try using the word when the feeling is toward self and then toward another.

SESSION 4—LEARNING TO FEEL SMALL

Theoretical Presentation

Many people believe that only those feelings which are massive and catastrophic are significant enough to deserve expression. It is true that occasionally all of us are subject to feelings which are gigantic, comprehensive, monstrous, and overpowering. It is also true that such important feelings will have to be resolved with the people most important to us.

To learn expressive skill, however, beginners have to begin at the beginning. The novice should examine simple, small feelings. For a person with a limited capacity to communicate feelings, it is good methodology to start with feelings which are *unimportant* on subjects which are *insignificant* with people and relationships which are *not threatening* and are, in fact, probably *expendable*. If we practice expressing concrete annoyances in the ordinary course of daily living, we will rarely have to deal with the ominous and the immense. If or when we do have to deal with large problems, we will have an accumulation of expressive skill to draw on.

Feelings have causes. They do not arise spontaneously out of nowhere. The search for simple causes of small feelings brings about the resolution of problems while they are still in an embryonic state, thus preventing the development of full-fledged difficulties.

In the search for small causes of small feelings, it can be helpful to consider specific factors. Today we will use the following: (a) time, (b) situation, (c) people, (d) money, (e) individual needs, and (f) expectations of others.

Organization

Participants are seated in groups around tables.

Equipment

Paper and pencil for each participant.

NOTE: This session confronts those who use denial and universalizing as a device to avoid feelings. It is a difficult lesson for the instructor.

Instructions

"Today we are going to examine and attempt to understand feelings that are related to small and very specific things.

"First, put your name in the top right-hand corner of your paper. Then think of a trivial annoyance which you have experienced during the past week. Write it down near the top of the sheet.

"As I pose a number of questions, think about the annoyance you have cited on your paper. In thinking about the questions, possibly you will find some clues to your feeling.

"First, let us consider the feeling from the point of view of *time*. How is your annoyance related to time? When do you feel annoyed—on specific days, at specific hours or specific moments? What came before the feeling? With what people have you previously experienced that particular feeling? Do your recollections of the past shed any light on your feeling in the present situation? Consider the future. Do you anticipate any future actions or consequences as a result of having this feeling? Will dire events or situations result from your having the feeling?

"Write down (1) *Time*. Then write any connections that there may be between your feeling and time."

Activity

Participants follow directions.

Instructions

"Next, write down (2) *Situation*. Does your feeling arise in a particular place under particular circumstances? Where were you when the feeling of annoyance arose? What did the environment encompass?"

Activity

Participants follow directions.

Instructions

"Now consider the people involved. Write down (3) *People*. Who, specifically, is involved in your annoyance? There must be someone besides yourself. For purposes of this exercise, you cannot be annoyed with yourself. Put down a specific relationship or a specific name. You do not need to state the name in such a way that others can identify the individual.

"Are there other people besides the one you have written? If so, write down the names of any other people who are consistently involved in the same annoyance.

"Does your annoyance have to do with the relationship between certain people in the situation? Is it related to an alliance or union of people acting with you or people acting in collusion against you?

"Under (3) *People,* write down the names of people and facts related to relationships that contribute to your annoyance."

Activity
Participants follow directions.

Instructions
"Now write down (4) *Money.* Does money have anything to do with your annoyance? What amount of money? What aspect of the use of money annoyed you? Did you lose it or gain it? Earn it or squander it? Save it or spend it? Give it or receive it? Risk it or protect it? Is there a relationship with past or future expenditures? Under (4) *Money,* write ways in which money is related to your annoyance."

Activity
Participants follow directions.

Instructions
"Now think about your individual needs. Is your annoyance related to the satisfaction or nonsatisfaction of some need you feel? What need? Write down (5) *My Needs* and under it, relate your annoyance to your particular needs."

Activity
Participants follow directions.

Instructions

"Is your annoyance related to the expectations of others? Write down (6) *Expectations of Others*. Tell how your annoyance is related to the standards or expectations of others. Your hair-do? Clothes? Appearance? Weight? Intelligence? Knowledge? Skill? Extent of participation?

"Discuss your papers with others at your table. Attempt to help each other be specific in cases when the person is unable to do so. Ask questions of each other in the search for specific aspects of your annoyance."

Activity

Participants work in their groups around each table, attempting to help each other complete their papers.

Instructions

"Let us now talk as a whole group. What kinds of experiences have you had in attempting to be specific in your feelings?"

Activity

Members of the group suggest any points they care to make. These are written on the chalkboard as a summary of the discussion.

Instructions

"Were some of you more skillful in being specific than the others in your group? Were there certain members of your group who seemed to show special ability in being specific?

"I will collect your papers and analyze them. In another period we can have further discussion. We can use as teachers those you have suggested today as having special skill in being specific. I may be able to discover others with unusual degrees of insight as revealed in the written papers. These people should be able to help the rest learn to be more specific in the expression of feelings."

Activity

If members of the class seem interested, the topic may be pursued in another one or two periods of discussion.

SESSION 5—GUIDELINES FOR FEELING EXPRESSION

Certain methods of expressing feelings produce more catharsis and contribute to a better problem-solving process than other means of expression.

The following criteria for effective verbal expression of feelings may provide an evaluative checklist. With it, you will be able to check your own expressions in the next emotogenic situation and determine whether or not you have been able to accomplish effective expression.

Directness. Expressing the feeling to the person who engendered it, not to someone unrelated to the stimulus.

Verbalization. Using words which are specifically descriptive and accurately expressive.

Relevance. Describing the provoking stimulus, not some other person, object, or context.

Definitiveness. Defining and limiting the emotion to its specific type or category, to its exact duration, to a specific stimulus, and a particular person in a limited context or situation.

Subjectivity. Placing the locus of the emotion clearly within the self, eliminating imagined feelings of others or generalizing the feeling.

Proportion. Expressing the exact degree of the feeling, neither minimizing nor exaggerating it.

Exhaustiveness. Expressing all that is felt related to the specific stimulus, leaving no residual.

Appropriateness. Expressing the feeling at a suitable time and place, avoiding involvement of those not involved in the stimulus.

Promptness. Expressing the feeling at the first appropriate time, without undue delay or postponement.

Consistency. Expressing each feeling as it arises so that the response can be limited to one difficulty or stimulus and problems do not build up.

NOTE: Ten criteria for effective feeling expression are presented. These may be presented as a lecture or they may be developed into a series of sessions checking individual behavior in specific encounters outside the class. Or the criteria may be presented intermittently between other sessions as a checklist.

UNIT II—AMBIVALENCE

SESSION 1—"BY THE TIME I GET TO PHOENIX"

Organization

BY PASSING OUT numbered slips, the leader divides the class into groups consisting of six, seven or eight persons. Chairs are arranged in circles.

Equipment

A record player and the record "By the Time I Get to Phoenix," sung by Glen Campbell (Capitol 2015); paper and pencils for each group.

Activity

With no preliminary explanation, the leader writes three questions on the board.

1. How does she feel about him?
2. How does he feel about her?
3. Why does he leave her?

"By the Time I Get to Phoenix" is played. When the record is finished, each group is asked to discuss the three questions.

Instructions

"Write the conclusions of your group discussion on the paper you have been given. Write the answers to each question on separate sheets. Indicate which question is being answered."

Activity

Group members discuss the questions and write their composite answers on the separate sheets of paper. After about twenty minutes, each group is asked to give a report of their

NOTE: A currently familiar song is used for this session, though any song which highlights an ambivalent situation could be used.

discussion. Group answers are collected, collated by the instructor, and posted on the bulletin board.

Theoretical Summary

Positive emotions are rarely experienced as totally positive, unclouded by negative emotions; negative emotions are rarely experienced as totally unbrightened by positive emotions. Most of our feeling experiences are characterized by complexity and chaos. When simultaneous *good* feelings and *bad* feelings are experienced toward the same object or person and when the feelings are accompanied by confusion and indecisiveness, the state is called *ambivalence. Valence* or *valency* means having worth or value. *Ambi-* means both, around or on both sides. *Ambivalence* is the coexistence of opposite or conflicting feelings about one person, object, or situation, when the feelings are equated in importance.

Most of our polite social relationships and interchanges are confined to positive expressions and approval. It is far easier to feel related to a person who is praising us than to one who is expressing anger, annoyance, or criticism. Small, positive talk is indeed the rule in casual social situations.

A significant intimate relationship, however, requires both positive and negative expressions. Yet when the persons intimately involved fear the loss of the relationship, they often express only their positive feelings, reserving their negative expressions for casual relationships in the stores or on the street. Such one-sided expression creates a residue of unsolved problems, disguised in such unidentified emotions as confusion, indecision, nervousness, depression, or a similar vague state.

Negative expressions become tolerable and even interesting when the overall positive relatedness is quite clear and wholly secure. A wide spectrum of expressiveness widens the areas of shared concern, activates differentiation between the persons involved, and makes possible satisfying joint decisions and effective action.

The ability to tolerate complex, pervading ambivalent feelings without succumbing either to avoidance or precipitous action is characteristic of the mentally healthy person.

Assignment for the Next Lesson

"Please come to the next class with examples of your own ambivalent feelings. Be prepared to state the two conflicting or opposite feelings, and the person toward whom they are directed. Your considerations should be limited to ambivalence toward a person only."

Response of the Pilot Group: Collation

How Does She Feel About Him?

He is a roamer, but she accepts what he is.

He is her security. She loves him in a possessive, selfish way.

She feels she has to hide her real feelings—how much she loves him—for fear of getting hurt.

She treats him like an old shoe. She takes him for granted.

She feels dependent on him, but she can't afford to let him know this or let him get too close to her.

She doesn't listen to his warning. She doesn't think he'd really leave, no matter what. She is sure he cannot do without her.

When he leaves, she feels emptiness, rejection.

How Does He Feel About Her?

He is beginning to feel he really loves her, but does not want marital responsibilities. He is not sure of his own needs.

He loves her in his own way because she is undemanding. He feels she is immature and is frustrated by her lack of mature response.

He feels trapped. He feels manipulated and taken for granted. He feels dominated and martyred.

He cares a lot about her and depends on her. He knows she loves him and wants her to show it.

He is angry with her because she can't fulfill all his needs. Finally, he can't stand it.

Maybe he loves her too much and knows he must leave before it gets too deep. He feels that she will know how much she loves him only when she sees he is really gone. But he wants a place to come back to.

Why Does He Leave Her?

He is immature and is leaving for good this time to be free of responsibility. He has left before. He wants to prove he really will leave, not just threaten over and over.

His last remnant of self-respect causes him to leave a hopeless situation. When he gives up all hope of change, he leaves, inflicting punishment on her and on himself. He tells himself that he is leaving her for her own good, hoping she will find something more permanent.

He leaves to prove that he can do without her. He cannot face the responsibiilty of her dependence. He loves her but he loves his freedom more.

He is unsure of her love for him. He doesn't feel she really loves him, so he leaves to end the rejection he feels. He feels she can do without him, too.

He knows he loves her, but still he abandons her. He feels frustrated and hopeless, guilty about leaving her.

It is hard for him to leave her.

I think he will come back.

SESSION 2—SELF-BLACKOUT BINGO

Organization

Participants are seated around tables in groups of three or four.

Equipment

Sheets of 12 x 18 in. manila tagboard, several jars of rubber cement for each table, felt-tipped marking pens; pieces of colored construction paper, 2 x 3 in., in gray, yellow, fuchsia and black. Any other two colors may be used, but the colors should be complementary and give some connotation of positive and negative. The black is important, since it will stand for blackout.

Activity

The instructor passes out the equipment, providing each person with one sheet of manila tagboard and a felt-tipped pen, plus a supply of various colored paper tags and a jar of rubber cement for each table.

Instructions

"Work with your tagboard with the long dimension held horizontally. Write your name in the bottom right-hand corner of your sheet of cardboard.

"Think of the person in your life toward whom you are the most ambivalent, that is, toward whom your positive and negative emotions are most confused. Write this person's name on the gray tag and paste it in the center of your paper."

Activity

Participants follow directions.

Instructions

"On the yellow slips of paper, write all of the positive feelings you have toward this person. Write one feeling on each slip of paper. Paste these slips of paper on the right-hand side of the

---

NOTE: This session is quite complicated, and may span several sessions. It will be necessary for the instructor to follow the instructions carefully to achieve the desired response: SHOCK!

manila tag board. Write all the positive feelings you can recall. You may have the entire right side of your manila board covered with slips of yellow paper."

Activity

Participants follow directions concerning the yellow slips of paper.

Instructions

"On the fuchsia slips of paper, write all of the negative feelings you have toward this person. Write one feeling on each slip of paper. Paste these slips of paper on the left-hand side of the board. Write as many negative feelings as you can recall. You may have the entire left side of the cardboard covered with slips of fuchsia paper." (It may take a whole session to complete this part of the exercise. If so, the second part of the exercise may be held over until the next period.)

"Has everyone finished pasting his papers? If so, we can proceed. Look at the colored papers on your sheet. If you have written any feelings which are not really feelings—but are something else—draw a line around those papers, outlining the paper with your pen."

Activity

Participants follow the directions as best they can. There will probably be questions, but the instructor will answer no questions related to content but will refer them back to the asker. The instructor may, however, further clarify the directions. Each person must decide for himself whether what he has written is a feeling. If he wishes, he may refer any question to his group.

Instructions

"Now, pull off and throw away all the colored papers you have outlined.

"With your pen, draw a line around any paper which is a feeling not originating within yourself. If it is not something you yourself feel toward the person in the center—but is instead a feeling the other person has about you—outline the paper with your pen. Then pull off and throw away all the colored papers you have just outlined."

Activity

Participants follow directions. The instructor pauses until each succeeding stage is completed.

Instructions

"Put a black paper on any of the feelings you often pretend to yourself you do not have. If frequently you pretend that this feeling does not exist, put a black paper over it. Paste down all the black papers."

Activity

Participants follow directions.

Instructions

"Put a black paper over all the feelings you have never acknowledged *verbally* to the person in the center, all those that you have never told the person you feel. Verbal acknowledgment does not mean throwing dishes, spending money, getting drunk, or slamming doors."

Activity

Participants follow directions.

Instructions

"If you have been deceptive with the person regarding the nature of your feeling, black that feeling out. If you usually pretend to the other person that you have a good feeling when it is really a bad feeling, or if you pretend it is a bad feeling when it is really a good feeling, put a black paper over it. If you have pretended it is very important when it is quite unimportant, black that feeling out. If you have pretended it is unimportant when it is really very important to you, black it out."

Activity

Participants follow directions. (By this time, many of the participants will have nothing left on their papers. Everything has been torn off or covered up.)

Instructions

"Think about the person on the gray tag in the center. If you do not want the person in the center to know you are ambivalent, draw a line around the gray tag."

Activity

Participants follow directions.

Instructions

"If you have drawn a line around the gray paper in the center, pull off that paper and throw it away."

(At this point there are likely to be strong responses from the participants, such as "I can't throw away my husband," etc.)

Activity

Despite protests, participants follow the directions.

Instructions

"We are going to have a public exhibit of all of your papers. I am going to post them on the wall of the gymnasium for everyone to see. You cannot black out your name. You may black out or tear off everything on your paper except your name. You are not allowed to cover up your name.

"If you have any further feelings you do not want to exhibit, put a black paper over them too. If you don't want people to see the person toward whom you are ambivalent, you may black out the gray paper also."

Activity

Participants follow the directions.

Instructions

"Now discuss the following questions with the members of your group."

Questions for Discussion

1. If you have not been willing to acknowledge ambivalence in feelings, what have you done to yourself?
2. If you have not been willing to express feelings of ambivalence, what have you done to the object of your ambivalence?

3. How did your ambivalence come about?
4. Why is ambivalence such a problem?
5. What positive feelings were most predominant? What negative feelings?

Response of the Pilot Group: Summary of Discussion

Ambivalence was shown more toward the spouse than toward any other family member.

Dependency is a factor correlated with ambivalence of feeling.

The most predominant positive feeling expressed was love. Fully one-third of the positive feelings expressed were love. Almost one-sixth of the positive feelings were respect and admiration.

The most predominant negative feeling expressed was hate. People also feel ambivalent toward themselves.

SESSION 3—POSITIVE AND NEGATIVE FEELINGS

Theoretical Presentation

Though emotions are neither inherently good nor bad, we all tend to place values on emotions. We classify as *good* those emotions which are accompanied by a sense of confident well-being: cooperation, warmth, love, commonality, empathy, fairness, closeness or belonging. Certain other emotions produce nervousness, trembling, queasiness, and diffused anxiety, and threaten our sense of well-being; therefore, we classify such feelings as envy, hate, fear, jealousy, or covetousness as bad emotions.

Depending upon their experience, some individuals classify as good those emotions which others classify as bad. For example, trust is ordinarily considered as a positive emotion. However, trust is a bad emotion to one who feels that his trust has caused him to be cheated, rejected, or hurt. Instead of nurturing trust, he would like to be rid of this feeling.

In interpersonal interactions, the expression of positive feelings is generally approved and sanctioned, whereas the expression of negative feelings may bring disapproval and censure. "If you can't say something that's real nice—then don't say anything at all is my advice."

When positive emotions are experienced or expressed in a relatively pure form, they do not produce a sense of disturbance or trauma. An excess of pure, unadulterated happiness brings no one to a psychiatrist.

However, even the awareness of lurking negative feelings produces guilt, tension, and anxiety in many people. They have difficulty in acknowledging the presence of negative feelings, much less expressing them. Such people say of themselves, "I like everybody." "I look for the good in every person," etc. Havelock Ellis wrote that it is in the lunatic asylum that such optimism flourishes.

It is not because some feelings are *bad* or *sick* that psychiatry

---

NOTE: This session embodies a technique used fairly frequently throughout the book: division of the class into two groups typifying certain bipolar traits and using each group as a catalyst for the other group. Receptivity to change is the trait rewarded.

is concerned chiefly with negative emotions, ambivalence, and bipolarity of feelings. It is because these are the feelings which are experienced as *trouble,* and psychiatry was devised to help *troubled* people.

Few people are able to express both positive and negative feelings with equivalent ease. Also to be found in hospitals are those who express anger and other negative feelings with ease but find it virtually impossible to express positive feelings.

In this session we will attempt to equalize our abilities.

Organization

Regular classroom seating. Later, chairs will be pushed back to make an area in which class members can move about freely. A nearby room or area should be available for division of the class into separate groups.

Equipment

Tags of red and green construction paper, 2 x 3 in., with one tag of each color for each participant; small round dots of red and green paper made by punching holes in the paper with a hole punch, envelopes or other containers in which to keep the red and green dots, one jar of rubber cement for each four or five participants, several rolls of transparent tape in dispensers, one pencil for each participant.

Instructions

"If you were to classify yourself as one type or the other, which would you call yourself? If you have difficulty expressing negative feelings, select a green tag. If it is easy for you to tell people you like them but hard for you to criticize or tell people you are angry with them, put on a green tag. Write your name on the bottom of the tag, and attach it to your shoulder with the transparent tape.

"If you have difficulty expressing positive feelings, select a red tag. If it is easy for you to tell people you are angry with them, but hard for you to compliment them or tell them you like them, put on a red tag. Write your name on the bottom of the tag and attach it to your shoulder with the tape.

"You must classify yourself one way or the other."

Activity

Each participant selects an appropriate tag, writes his name on it and attaches it to his shoulder.

Instructions

"I will give each of the green tags some tiny green dots. I will give each of the red tags some tiny red dots.

"All of you who are wearing green tags are to stay here. All of you who are wearing red tags, go to the next room and wait there for me. I am going to give separate instructions to each color group."

Activity

All participants wearing red tags go to the separate room. The instructor first gives instructions to the green-tag people who remain in the classroom.

Instructions to the Green Tags

"When the two groups are together again, you are to be particularly pleasant to the red-tag people. Be extremely courteous and complimentary. Try to express positive affection. If the red-tag person returns your overtures with positive, friendly responses, or if he says or does anything nice in return, give him a small green dot.

"Are there any questions? Does everyone understand the procedure? Please wait here in the classroom. I will be back when I have given instruction to the red-tag people."

Instructions to Red Tags

"When the two groups get back together, you are to do annoying things to the green-tag people. You can make offensive remarks, step on their toes, poke them, grab something from them, or do whatever else you think will annoy them.

"If the green-tag person is able to tell you to stop, to tell you that your behavior annoys him, or to express any clearly negative feeling, give him a red dot. Now return to the classroom, and we will proceed with the exercise."

Instructions to Combined Groups

"Talk only to those people who have a tag of the opposite color. If you are given one of the small dots, be careful to save it."

Activity

Participants move freely around the room, talking to those with tags of the opposite color. The activity continues until ten or fifteen minutes before the end of the period or until interest subsides, whichever is sooner.

Instructions

"Now return to your chairs.

"If you were a green-tag person, and you responded with the negative response which was difficult for you, the red-tag person who initiated the interchange gave you a small red dot for a prize. If you were a red-tag person and you responded with the positive response which was difficult for you, the green-tag person who initiated the interchange gave you a small green dot for a prize. You received a prize only for a response contrary to your usual mode of behavior.

"I deliberately made the dots very small and awkward, because changing oneself is usually quite awkward and the changes accomplished are usually very small. Nevertheless, small changes have significance.

"You will find a number of jars of rubber cement available. Paste your prize dots on the top of your tags above your name. The number of dots on your tag will show how much you have managed to change yourself during this period."

Activity

Participants paste the dots on their name tags, which are posted on the bulletin board at the end of the period. In the class time remaining, the instructor conducts a discussion related to the types of experiences encountered in the process of completing the exercise.

Questions for Discussion

1. How many of you were able to win dots of the opposite color? Were you aware of responding in an unfamiliar way?

2. Is there anyone who failed to win any dots? Do you know why? Can you explain it to the rest of us?
3. Were there any responses that were of special interest or importance? Which color tag gave the response?
4. What general conclusions have you about positive and negative feelings?
5. What general conclusions have you about the process of self-change?

Response of the Pilot Group

Those Having Difficulty Expressing Negative Feelings

"I have no difficulty recognizing anger toward myself, but I do with anger toward others."

"I fight against negative feelings. I keep them bottled up."

"Expressing negative feelings makes me feel guilty—like a gossipper."

Those Having Difficulty Expressing Positive Feelings

"I recognize negative feelings without difficulty. I can't recognize positive feelings in myself or others."

"I cannot express positive feelings. I just take them for granted."

"I enjoy being hostile most of the time."

Those Making Ambivalent Responses

"I had difficulty determining which was positive and which was negative."

"I changed roles—from a green tag to a red tag—during the exercise."

General Conclusions

"Positive and negative feelings are difficult to separate."

"Feelings change, so that a once-positive feeling may change into a negative feeling."

"A person expressing a positive feeling wants reciprocation of the same feeling to the same degree."

"Expression makes you vulnerable."

SESSION 4—CHANGING AMBIVALENCE TO MULTIVALENCE

Better it is to bow than breake.

JOHN HEYWOOD
Proverbs, Part I, Chapter IX

It is computed, that eleven thousand persons have, at several times, suffered death, rather than submit to break their eggs at the smaller end.

JONATHAN SWIFT
Gulliver's Travels, Part I, Chapter IV

The bow too tensely strung is easily broken.

PUBLILIUS SYRUS
Maxim 388 (circa 42 B.C.)

It is a bad plan that admits of no modification.

PUBLILIUS SYRUS
Maxim 469 (circa 42 B.C.)

Theoretical Presentation

Since ambivalence is an inevitable part of the living process, the resolution of conflict related to ambivalence is crucial to the achievement of mental health.

Conflict must be accepted as a core experience in living. Pathology is not produced simply by simultaneous presence of opposite feelings. Pathology results from an inability to tolerate opposing feelings and at the same time commit oneself to action involving only one of the feelings. Without such tolerance and such commitment, the sufferer attempts to block out one of the feelings or swings back and forth frantically from one feeling to another.

The rigid person tends to polarize feelings into two categories that are diametrically opposed—love and hate, good and bad, warmth and coldness, etc. Such rigidity makes him actually fear variety in alternatives. He believes that he will be incapable of making a choice or finding a solution if he allows himself any degree of flexibility.

Problems can be approached in a different way when a person

NOTE: This session includes a lecture and a number of maxims extolling flexibility.

learns tolerance for conflicting feelings. For one thing, he gains time. Instead of two alternatives, his search can be for many—and for many shadings of each alternative. Specifically examining a problem and developing alternatives tends to depolarize feelings and allow scrutiny of smaller, less differentiated units. For our purposes we shall call this concept *multivalence* as opposed to *ambivalence*. We shall replace two values with many values. Instead of problem solving, we substitute problem modification. Minor modifications in the various elements of a problem will eventually produce major alterations in the nature of the problem itself.

If the ambivalence appears to be between love and hate, we can ask ourselves when specifically do we love? When specifically do we hate? Do we love our spouse on Tuesdays and hate on Fridays? (time). Do we love when in the house and hate when in the car? (context). Does the hatred arise when the spouse does not squeeze the toothpaste to our liking? Or is it when he stops at the tavern for a beer on his way home from work? (provocation). When we ask and answer such questions, we have broken ambivalences into smaller units, specifying feelings governed by time, context and provocation. Having done so, we are approaching a position when we will be able to consider a wide range of alternative solutions.

The whole approach to problem solving is altered if flexibility is viewed as inherently desirable. To be flexible when facing stress, to tolerate many conflicting values and to consider various courses of action are requisites of mental health. Not only does the mentally healthy person tolerate awareness of conflicting emotions but he is able to make decisions and take thoughtful action despite conflict. He entertains a modicum of indecisiveness, nostalgia, or regret. Resiliency, plasticity and rebound replace rigidity, brittleness, and tenacity. The black and white of right and wrong fades into shades of gray, which are more difficult to distinguish than two opposing values. Nevertheless, the blendings produce considerably less psychic disturbance and considerably more peace of mind.

Maxims for Dealing with Ambivalence

1. Acknowledge that ambivalence is inevitable, a basic part of living.
2. Recognize that the ability to accommodate large amounts of ambivalence without inordinate psychic disturbance or undue effort is a characteristic of mental health.
3. Develop a full spectrum of alternatives in each situation. Try to modify each alternative to make it more desirable and thus more acceptable.
4. Strive for flexibility and adaptability to circumstances.
5. Try to alter problems rather than to solve or eliminate them. Instead of trying to solve problems, look for ways to minimize problems, modify consequences, dilute painful results.
6. Recognize that, despite ambivalence, action may still be taken. Take it.

Section III

Self-Communication

UNIT I—INNER SPACE WALK

SESSION 1—THE SEARCH FOR ROCKS FROM INNER SPACE
WHY DO ANYTHING?

Why sail Westward out of Renaissance Europe, at ruinous cost, and risk falling off the edge of the world?

To see what's over there.

And to find a new world, green and virgin, rich and full of gold. And full of hope.

Why poke about under 19th-Century microscopes, facing ridicule and hunger and the waste of a lifetime?

To see what's down there.

And to find new microworlds, full of cures and knowledge of ourselves. And full of hope.

Why do anything? Why go to the moon, the planets and the stars?

To see what's out there.

Somehow inevitably to make us more than we are. To push back the edges as long as there are edges to push back. To find unimaginable new answers, inexpressible new excitements, ineffable new hope.

For whenever and wherever man has gone looking before, to see what was there, he has been right to do so. And he has never gone unrewarded.[1]

Theoretical Presentation

THE PRECEDING QUOTATION, specifically related to the moon walk, applies aptly to the process of communication. Though one may present numerous reasons to show that communication is both desirable and necessary, the most significant reason for communication is actually self-exploration.

That the scientist must approach investigation without prejudice is a basic scientific tenet. Premature judgments limit the exploratory process. Evaluative judgments come properly when the exploratory period has been completed.

---

[1] Advertisement for LTV Aerospace Corporation, printed in celebration of the first landing on the moon. *Dallas Times Herald,* July 25, 1969.

The astronauts made an incredible space voyage in an attempt to land on the moon and discover its secrets. When they gathered rock samples from the moon's surface, they had no way of knowing whether a rock contained valuable or useless elements, or whether it had potential life-creating properties or carried infectious particles of deadly disease.

Similarly, when we transcend our realistic boundaries and explore the nature of our own inner space, we must gather and examine data without drawing conclusions based on preconceived ideas about ourselves. Each individual must make the long voyage through his own inner space solely for the purpose of discovering what is there.

Why explore inner space? Because it is the only inner area we will ever be privileged to explore. We can know only little of the inner space of another human being. When the first two astronauts walked on the moon, each had a solitary experience. Millions of television viewers watched them; each watcher may well have identified with the astronauts and imagined himself striding on the moon's surface; yet only those two walkers really knew what it was like on the moon at that moment; and of those two people, neither knew what it was actually like to the other. Thus we may share experiences with other people, we may observe others in the process of their experience, we may identify or empathize with other people, but we can never know what living feels like to anyone else.

When the first astronaut came down the ladder and stepped on the moon's surface, he found immediately that he could walk without great difficulty, and his exhilaration was apparent. Likewise, the person who travels in his own inner space experiences similar liberation when he finds that he can walk without too much difficulty. His ability to master the situation, despite the strangeness of the setting, brings him confidence. He experiences a feeling of liberation from the terrors previously related to the unknown when he takes an imaginary walk in his own inner space, opening his eyes to see all that is there and collecting evidence for further study, comparison, and contemplation.

Communication is an essential part of the process of discovery.

Not only are the results of inquiry into the nature of one's own inner space more enjoyable when they are communicated to others but it is only when his results are shared that the individual becomes fully aware of the exact nature of his own discoveries. He is then able to experience the dissipation and dissolution of age-old fears and terrors.

In many instances, a tremendous change in feeling results from a small amount of communication on an insignificant discovery. Vastly greater than the significance of the act of discovery are the release, catharsis, liberation, and sense of well-being that come from inner exploration and communicated concepts of one's inner self. "One small step in inner space—a giant leap in insight."

Organization

Usual seating. Participants are later to be dispatched elsewhere.

Equipment

For each participant, a felt-tipped marking pen and six to eight pieces, approximately 3 x 6 in., of gray construction paper, cut into jagged shapes; a box approximately the size of a dress box, a roll of 3-in. brown gummed tape.

Instructions

"Each person will receive a marking pen and six to eight pieces of gray construction paper cut into jagged shapes. These pieces of paper are rocks to be found in an unexplored territory. You are to leave the room and take a walk. Find a quiet spot and sit down in solitary contemplation. Imagine you are taking a walk in inner space. You are walking on the surface of your own inner space. On this surface you find some rocks. These rocks will be composed of your feelings—any that you find there. You will attempt to identify these rocks in your inner space— your feelings. Write the feelings that you find on these pieces of gray construction paper, each different feeling on a different paper. Do not talk to anyone during this exercise. Stay entirely alone. Think to yourself. Feel within yourself.

"When you return to this room, we will place all your rocks in this box. Before the module leaves, we will seal up the box. We will carry the rocks back to earth for study. When we return to earth, we shall ask a group of scientists to study the rocks.

"Since I am asking you to write some very intimate feelings, do not put your names on the moon rocks. Usually in this class you are not allowed to be anonymous. However, today is an exception. Do not put your names on the rocks.

"Return to this room in twenty minutes. Do not be late, as the module might take off without you, and you would be left alone in inner space forever."

Activity

Participants leave with their pens and papers and go to various parts of the grounds to walk in inner space. When they return to the room, the rocks from inner space are placed in the box. When the allotted time has expired, the box is sealed. Those who return to the room after the box is sealed are not permitted to include their rocks in the discussion the following period.

SESSION 2—SCIENTIFIC EXAMINATION OF THE ROCKS
FROM INNER SPACE

Organization

Several tables are placed together at the center of the room to provide a large conference table at which the scientists will be seated. Members of the class are seated around the tables, as in an amphitheater.

Equipment

The sealed box of inner space rocks from the previous period; pencils and papers on which the scientists can write their reports.

Instructions

"We need a number of participants, perhaps six or eight, to serve as scientists examining our inner space rocks. These volunteers should enjoy study and research, and be able to classify items. Do I have some applicants for this scientific endeavor? Volunteers, come forward and sit at the conference table. All others, be seated in the outer ring of chairs."

Activity

The instructor waits until six or eight have volunteered and seated themselves at the center table and the remainder of the class have been seated in the outer rings.

Instructions

"During this period, only the scientists seated at the table can talk. The rest of you are sitting in a one-way vision room. You can watch the scientists at work, you can hear what they say, but you cannot participate in their conversations or discussions.

"Scientists, you are now to unseal the box of rocks and begin your scientific task of classifying the rocks from inner space. After about twenty minutes, we will ask you for a report on the nature of inner space. The scientists should select a chairman to conduct the meeting and make the report."

Activity

After selecting their chairman, the scientists unseal the box and attempt to sort the rocks. Members of the observing group view their own rocks and hear them discussed anonymously and compared to others. After twenty minutes, the chairman makes his report.

Response of the Pilot Group: Report of the Scientists

The majority of the feelings were negative, which is not surprising. Most of the rocks from inner space dealt with fears—the most common of which was fear of the uncertainty of life—what is held for us, and a fear of how we would react to it. There was an expression of a fear of failure and of hopelessness because of being in a mental hospital. There was a fear of the future, of not being able to leave the hospital, of life outside the hospital, of jobs and responsibilities. There was a fear of not having an adequate amount of self-confidence to deal with life's situations, to speak, to make decisions, to face life without fear.

There was a desire to express feelings honestly and a fear of expressing feelings, presumably because of the criticism one has to confront when expressing feelings.

One person felt guilt over receiving without deserving, a sense of worthlessness and inferiority.

One expressed love for a young son—a new experience.

One discovered love and trust heretofore not apparent.

There was a frustrated ambition to contribute to society.

In conclusion, the scientists recommend that for future classes we explore the how's and why's of the most frequent negative feelings in an effort to understand ourselves better.

UNIT II—SELF-MESSAGES

SESSION 1—SOURCES AND CONTENT OF SELF-MESSAGES

> Enough to thee the small still voice aye thundering in thine inner ear.
>
> SIR RICHARD FRANCES BURTON
> *The Kasidah of Haji Abdu El-Yazdi*, IX, 19

Theoretical Presentation

ALL OF US RECEIVE messages from what we most frequently call the *voice of conscience.* These messages are primarily proverbs, adages, admonitions, exhortations, and warnings given us repeatedly by our parents to help us learn to control our behavior and establish parentally approved action consonant with the mores of our society. Whenever our own needs and desires conflict with the teachings of our authority figures, we are forced, at whatever cost, to reconcile the disparate messages in order to act.

Let us examine these messages to ourselves and see if we can find enlightenment in regard to our conflicts and our behavior.

Organization

Participants are seated at tables, in groups of four to six.

Equipment

Pencil and paper for each participant.

Instructions

"Write your name in the top right-hand corner of your paper. Think for a few minutes what you invariably tell yourself when you are in a stressful situation. Write down what you tell yourself."

NOTE: This session is quite provocative of self-examination. The instructor may have difficulty categorizing the self-messages submitted. The discussion is valuable without this step, however.

Activity

Class members write down the messages. After writing is finished, participants conduct group discussions at each table.

Instructions

"In your groups, discuss the following questions regarding sources of self-messages. Set down your conclusions as a group report."

Questions for Discussion

1. Can you identify the primary source of the messages you tell yourself? Proverbs? Bible? Literature? Cliché? Folk saying?
2. Can you separate the messages which came from your mother and the messages which came from your father? Are the messages different?
3. Do some of your messages come from other sources, such as older brothers and sisters? Other relatives? Teachers? Ministers? Others?

Instructions

"Now, discuss your individual lists. Attempt to classify the content of the messages according to topics. Your categories may be overlapping and confusing, but try to make a classification. Write the categories in parentheses after the messages. Work as a group."

Activity

Participants work until the end of the period, when the instructor collects the group reports and the individual papers. Before the next session, the instructor classifies the messages and posts the collation on the bulletin board. The posted collation promotes further discussion and encourages participants to make interpersonal comparisons.

Response of the Pilot Group: Quotations

Sources of Messages

"Standards are derived from parents."

"Folklore and proverbs are the major sources of parental concepts."

"Parental attitudes are very influential in forming our attitudes and controlling our behavior, even though we thought our parents were wrong."

"There is a discrepancy between what parents say and what they do. Parental actions speak louder than parental words."

Messages Related to Feelings

"Control your anger."

"Don't lose your temper or you'll kill your father. His heart can't take it."

"Talk softly. Don't raise your voice."

"Children should be seen and not heard."

"Always smile regardless of what happens."

"Don't let your feelings show."

"Do not talk back."

"Don't get on a high horse."

"Be a nice girl and hush crying."

"You may be unhappy, but you don't have to let anyone know it."

Messages Related to Values

"Honesty is always the best policy."

"An evil thought is the same as an evil deed."

"If at first you don't succeed, try, try again."

"Any job worth doing is worth doing right."

"You can do anything you want if you want to badly enough."

"Be patient with yourself."

"Failure and success are measured by income."

"Criticism is the same as failure."

"You should not fail because you are capable of everything."

"Hitch your wagon to a star."

"He can who thinks he can."

"Honor thy father and thy mother."

Messages Related to Sexual Identification

"If you are not a good wife, you are a failure."

"Nice girls don't smoke."

"Ladies are reserved and don't use strong language."

"A woman must not enjoy food."

"Men don't cry."

"Sex is man's pleasure and woman's duty."

Messages of Self-Recrimination

"I'd look great ten pounds lighter."

"Why do I do that!"

"I've done so many awful things, I deserve being punished by others."

"I have no special talent—nothing to give."

"I'm so impatient, demanding, and picky with my family."

"Maybe I can do that, but probably not."

"I shouldn't hurt my family when they've done so much for me."

Messages of Self-Exhortation

"Stop doing that and do first things first."

"Get a job."

"Drive carefully."

"Don't have such a one-track mind."

"Don't bite your nails."

"I've got to be more tolerant, patient, considerate, less accusing, more trusting."

"Never put off till tomorrow what should be done today."

Messages Expressing Rebellion

"I know I'm right, but I dare not say so."

"You are not going to dictate to me."

"I'll do it, but in my own time."

"I've got a perfect excuse, but I refuse to use it."

"Honestly!"

"Do it *their* way."

"I can't take any more."

"Oh, Mother!"

"A brassy mind-attitude is natural for me."

"I won't get mad no matter what they do."

"I want to live my own life."

Messages Concerning Interpersonal Relationships

"You are known by the company you keep."

"Do unto others as you would have them do unto you."

"You are sending me to the grave."

"Birds of a feather flock together."

"My husband isn't where he told me or doing what he told me. He's cheating behind my back."

"Our daughter is making poor grades just to hurt me and pay me back."

"My family purposely ignores the things I ask them to do."

"I'm unjustly accused of many actions."

"It seems that no one understands me."

Messages Expressing Wishes

"I wish something great would happen to me but I know it never will."

"I wish I could get just one good break."

"I wish I had her luck. She's always lucky."

"I wish I had known then what I know now."

"I wish I knew what causes me to be upset."

SESSION 2—MOTHER SAYS, FATHER SAYS, I SAY

Theoretical Presentation

In order to attain maturity, we must examine honestly the concepts, values, and admonitions of our parents and other authority figures. Some concepts we will accept; some we will choose to reject. We will accept part of some and reject part of some. Finally, after the sorting has been completed, we will incorporate certain parental values as our own values. The sources of the fully incorporated values will no longer be easily distinguishable. Instead, we will see all values as belonging to ourselves rather than our parents. The basic task of adolescence—and the precursor of maturity—is to scrutinize parental values and choose those to be accepted and those to be rejected. Most of us do not complete this complex task during our adolescent period. In fact, we may spend the greater part of our lives seeking its accomplishment.

Organization

Participants are in the same groups as in the preceding session.

Equipment

Pencil and paper for each participant, individual lists of self-messages written during the previous period, a mimeographed list of discussion questions for each group.

Activity

The instructor passes out pencil, paper, and each individual's self-messages. The groups discuss the questions on the mimeographed sheets.

Questions for Discussion

1. In your self-messages, do you refer to yourself as *I* or *you?* Is this significant?
2. Do you recall the situation, circumstance, or incident related to any particular message?

NOTE: In this session, participants further examine their self-messages and discuss their own values.

3. Do you remember when you first began giving yourself that message?
5. When do you ordinarily give that message to yourself?
5. Are your messages principally positive or negative?
6. Do your messages tell you what to feel or what not to feel? Do the messages tell when you should or should not express your feelings? How you should express them?
7. Do the messages tell you what to do or what not to do? When or how you should act?
8. Do you obey your self messages or do you rebel against them? Does your obedience get you into trouble? Does your rebellion get you into trouble? How? What kind of trouble?
9. Do you still believe what your mother taught you? Do you still believe what your father taught you? What your teachers taught you? Do their values still guide your behavior?
10. What parts of your parental messages have you accepted as yours? What parts have you rejected?

Activity

At the conclusion of the group discussion, each participant itemizes the ways in which he has accepted or rejected messages derived from parents.

Response of the Pilot Group: Collation

Now, I choose my own goals in life and rebel against the concepts I do not accept.

I choose to respect my parents when they are worthy of respect.

I do not choose to believe that the family should stick together under all circumstances.

I choose to consider my family "not close" because we do not share feelings.

I believe that a parent's love is not always equally divided among his children.

I choose to view older people individually and decide if they are wiser.

I choose to honor those people who deserve honor.

I choose to dress and act properly sometimes, but on other occasions, I choose to dress carelessly and to act spontaneously.

I choose to believe that good will not always overcome evil.

I choose not to do my best at every task. Some tasks are not worth time, money or energy.

I choose to be partly kind and partly unkind—kind when the circumstances call for kindness and unkind when the situation calls for unkindness.

I choose to be selfish to a certain extent—to be thoughtful of others but not to the point where I am pleasing everyone but myself.

I choose to believe that lying is only partly bad, according to circumstances and individuals.

I choose guilt when I am at fault. I do not choose guilt when I am not at fault.

I do not choose morals that mean dirt and shame; I choose morals that mean courage and joy.

I choose to believe there is good and bad in everyone. Sometimes the good offsets the bad and sometimes the bad offsets the good.

I choose not to like everyone, but most people I choose to like.

I choose to believe that I have the capacity to make other people happy but that I am not obligated to do so.

I choose to be concerned about what other people think only when the other people are close and dear to me.

I choose to trust people I know can be trusted.

I choose not to expect all others to accept my love and to love me in return.

I choose to believe that some disagreements cannot be worked out.

I choose to listen to the problems of others and to make my problems heard when I cry for help.

I choose to be angry at times, even violent, as long as I don't harm anyone.

I choose not to sulk.

I choose to cry as an outlet for a hurt I feel inside.

I choose to get along without manipulating people.

I choose to believe that people I care about will not dislike me for expressing myself.

I choose myself to be the most important person in my own life.

As such a person, I choose to be responsible for what I say and do.

SESSION 3—SELF-EXHORTATION AS A DEVICE
FOR AVOIDING ACTION

No matter how full a reservoir of *maxims* one may possess, and no matter how good one's *sentiments* may be, if one has not taken advantage of every concrete opportunity to *act*, one's character may remain entirely unaffected for the better. With mere good intentions, hell is proverbially paved.

WILLIAM JAMES
Psychology, Chapter 10

Theoretical Presentation

Many of our self-communications are exhortative in nature. An exhortation is an utterance, discourse, or address conveying urgent advice or recommendations. Through self-exhortation, we deceive ourselves into believing that we are taking action, whereas in reality we are using the exhortation to avoid responsibility for action. When the advice or recommendations preclude action rather than furthering it, self-exhortation becomes "idle words."

This handy accomplishment is achieved in a number of ways. One of the most common is to exhort ourselves toward possessing traits we do not possess.

"I should maintain clean, open and honest relationships. I should be more direct in expressing my feelings."

"I need to be realistic and discipline myself."

"I need to pick up my courage and learn to face defeat."

"I need to keep my nose out of other people's business."

"I need to prove to myself that I have the determination to complete one thing before starting another."

Another common exhortative trick is to tell ourselves that we should not feel what we feel or that we should feel something we do not. Such effort is futile, for feelings neither appear nor disappear on demand.

"I must get over this feeling of being treated like a child."

NOTE: This session points up the frequency of the self-messages used for avoiding action or responsibility. Messages can be developed from the previous lesson so that they will be clearly related to statements made by participants in the specific group.

"I must learn to trust someone besides close kin."

"I must realize that my family is trying to help me."

"I must learn not to be afraid and not to run away from a situation in which I am afraid."

"I must admit failure."

Another common way in which we use exhortation to avoid action is to make the exhortation so general that it is never possible to translate it into action, nor is it possible to know when any aspect of an action has been carried out.

"I will do it under any circumstances and at all times."

"I will try to make myself understood at home and in public."

"I will keep an open mind and think positively."

"I must increase the scope of my life and my concepts of things vital to me."

Sometimes we exhort ourselves to self-acceptance regardless of our behavior, when in reality self-acceptance is only appropriate when behavior warrants it. In this connection, it is easy to confuse effort toward action with action itself, to confuse a promise to try with a firm commitment to act.

"I am being honest with myself and trying to cooperate."

"I must stop being a child and accept myself as an adult."

"I must realize that everyone has good days and bad days and not fall apart if I am in a bad mood or make a mistake."

"I must accept myself as a woman."

Sometimes we even go so far as to exhort ourselves to have *someone else do something!*

"I should be shown more confidence by my husband."

"I should be given more responsibility for myself, more freedom of decision."

"I should be more accepted in my group."

One of the major ways to avoid futile self-exhortation is to be specific in our approach to problem solving. Today we are going to deal with specificity.

Organization

Class members are seated in groups around tables, five to eight in a group.

Equipment
Paper and pencil for each participant.

Instructions
"Write your name in the top right-hand corner of the paper. Down the left-hand margin of your paper, space out evenly the words *problem, who, what, when, where, how.*

"To the right of the word *problem*, specify some problem which you have.

"Similarly, specify *who* is involved in the problem, *what* you can do about it, *when* you are going to do it, *where* you will take this action, and *how* the action is to be accomplished.

"Try not to use any of the avoidances we have listed. Do not exhort yourself to have characteristics you do not have. Do not tell yourself to feel something you do not feel, or not to feel something you do feel. Do not generalize. Suggest only that action which is within your control."

Activity
Participants first follow the basic instructions for filling out the paper, then continue to write about their own specific problems.

Instructions
"Now, read the papers of each of the other members of your group. Cross off any statements that you believe are avoidances of the type we have discussed. When you cross off a statement, write at the side why you are crossing it off. If you have any questions, discuss them with your group."

Activity
Groups around each table discuss the papers of all members and cross off statements according to the instructions. The instructor closes the session with a summary given in a jesting tone.

Theoretical Summary
If your goal is to avoid action altogether, you should devote considerable care to the way in which you exhort yourself.

First, always link two opposite ideas and connect them with a *but*.

I shouldn't work so hard, *but* I need the money.

I shouldn't get so angry, *but* he is so annoying.

It will require great time and effort to assure yourself that both propositions are absolutely equal—to be certain you are presenting yourself with an ambivalence which is beyond resolution. Always talk very generally and avoid the specific as if it were poison. If you exert sufficient care, you never ever need expect yourself to do anything significant about your problem!

SESSION 4—STICKS AND STONES

Sticks and stones can break my bones, but names can never hurt me.

Theoretical Presentation

This familiar children's chant suggests that name-calling does not cause physical harm. In actuality, most of us are extremely sensitive to the names others call us and are well aware that name-calling can and does cause psychological hurt. Most of us use name-calling in expressing hostility toward others.

Each of us has certain names which hurt or enrage us more than other names. Although we make vigorous denials, we object most to the names which reinforce a feeling we already have about ourselves.

The old proverb says, "If the shoe fits, wear it." In reality, we only try on shoes we think will fit. The person who has acted with what he himself believes to be total honesty will not object to an investigation of his honesty. The teetotaler will not object if someone asks him if he is an alcoholic. Only those names which mesh with our insecurities cause consternation. If we examine the names we do not like to be called, we can find important clues to our feelings about ourselves and the pictures we have of ourselves.

Organization

Participants are seated around tables, in groups of five to eight.

Equipment

Pencil and paper for each person.

Instructions

"Pretend that I am calling *you* the following names. Write down those items you know you would not like to have anyone say about you, what you know you would not like to be called. Write down every statement that would make you angry."

Activity

The instructor reads the following list:

1. "You're stupid."
2. "You're ignorant."
3. "You're rude."
4. "You're a liar."
5. "You're a spendthrift."
6. "You're a tightwad."
7. "You're just plain mean."
8. "You're selfish."
9. "You're too darn particular."
10. "You're messy. You like living in a pig sty."
11. "You're neglecting your family."
12. "You're a failure."
13. "You're too emotional."
14. "You push everyone around."
15. "You just don't care about anything."
16. "You're lazy."
17. "You take people for granted."
18. "You're a snob."
19. "You're too easygoing."

Instructions

"On your paper you have probably written several statements. Now select the one which would be the most distasteful to you— the statement which would make you the most angry if said to you. Circle that statement."

Activity

Participants follow the directions.

Instructions

"Now discuss with others in your group why a particular statement is more annoying to you than the other statements."

Activity

Groups around each table participate in the discussion. After approximately thirty minutes, the instructor reconvenes the class.

Instructions

"We will now make a tally to see which statements were the most inflammatory to the largest number of you. As I read the list, raise your hand if you have circled that particular statement."

Activity

As the instructor reads the list, a tally of the responses is written on the chalkboard. The statements considered most significant make appropriate topics for succeeding lessons, since they clearly indicate areas of psychological difficulty to group members.

Response of the Pilot Group: Instructor's Observations

In one class session, the following is the rank order of statements listed as most anger producing:

Failure	6	Push everyone around	3
Liar	6	Don't care	2
Neglect of family	5	Ignorant	1
Selfish	3	Rude	1

SESSION 5—FEAR OF FAILURE: ORIGAMI BIRDS

Prior Preparation Required

The instructor should practice making origami birds, should find someone in the group who knows how to make them, or should invite an outside person to the session to serve as instructor.

Organization

Tables are arranged in a circle. Later, one person who is serving as origami instructor will be inside the circle. Some members of the class will be seated at the tables and others will be standing behind those seated at the tables.

Equipment

Several sheets of origami paper for each participant.

Instructions

"The central figures in our lesson today will be those of you who objected to being called *failures*. All those who consider yourselves failures or who are greatly afraid of failing, be seated on the outside of the circle of tables.

"Serving as assistants today will be those who answered that names other than *failure* were more threatening to you. Each of you stand behind one of those seated at the tables. It will not matter if there are several people standing behind one person, or if one person has to stand behind two people.

"Mr. ...., in the center, is to be our instructor. He will teach you how to make origami birds. You probably know that the Japanese art of paper folding is a complex one. The origami bird is one example of this complex art.

"While those seated at the table are folding their papers into the birds, the persons standing behind them are to find fault

---

NOTE: This session is provocative, amusing and frustrating to participants. The origami bird was selected for the exercise because, to the author, it is the prototype of complexity and frustration. Any other project of complexity and intricacy could be selected. Instructions for making the bird may be found in any book on Japanese paper folding, such as Johnson, Pauline: *Creating with Paper: Basic Forms and Variations.* Seattle, University of Washington Press, 1958; or Sakade, Florence: *Origami: Japanese Paper Folding* (Book Two). Rutland, Tuttle, 1958.

with what they are doing, and suggest to them that they are failures. Those working at the tables may respond in any way they desire.

"You critics may find fault in whatever way seems appropriate. You are to suggest failure in every possible way.

"I believe we are ready to start. Are there any questions?

"If not, Mr. . . . ., will you teach us how to make a bird?"

Activity

Those seated at the tables follow the instructions for making an origami bird. The critics stand behind and make derogatory remarks that suggest failure.

At the conclusion of the work, the leader asks for the responses of those treated as *failures,* as well as the experiences of the critic participants engaged in the exercise.

Response of the Pilot Group: Summary of Discussion

Those making birds . . .

Refused to take it seriously.

Accepted the outside evaluation—agreed they were failures.

Avoided the evaluation by stating in advance that they would be failures.

Became angry and refuted the accusation.

Broke off the relationship by saying, "Shut up," "Go away," or "Do it yourself."

The voices of failure . . .

Laughed and joked inappropriately.

Did not know how to be critical.

Found the task unpleasant because they did not like to be criticized themselves.

Felt unpopular.

Summary

Those assigned to be critical had great difficulty with their task. Those who were being criticized cut off communication or were unable to be expressive.

SESSION 6—FAILURE AS A PROVOCATIVE PLOY:
TIDDLY-WINKS

Theoretical Presentation

When a person consistently acts like a failure or alleges that he is a failure, his actions and claims serve both as a rejection of others and a hostile provocation. The provocation produces reciprocal rejection that augments the sense of failure and leads to the production of further anger, resentment, and frustration.

Those persons who consistently place themselves in situations where they must fail, who consistently downgrade themselves and admit incompetence need to examine their behavior and consider its hostile components.

Organization

Class members are seated around tables, in groups of six to eight.

Equipment

One set of Tiddly-Winks for each table; soft coverings for the tables. The games may be played on the floor if the room is carpeted. Some Tiddly-Winks sets provide small squares of felt, which may be placed under the pieces when they are jumped. These obviate the need for a soft surface.

Instructions

"Today we need to separate those who feel themselves failures from persons for whom failure has not been a significant problem. If you have not been troubled by a sense of failure, go to the next room and wait there until you receive further instructions. It will be about ten minutes."

Activity

After the nonfailures leave, the instructor explains the activity to those who remain in the classroom, that is, those who have acknowledged their feelings of failure.

NOTE: This session aims at the use of self-effacement as a device for expressing hostility. The role reversal catches off-guard those who have this trait and forces self-examination.

Instructions to the Tiddly-Winks Teachers

"I am going to teach you how to play the old, simple game of Tiddly-Winks. After my explanation, you are to be the teachers. You will teach the game to those who are presently out of the room."

Activity for Tiddly-Winks Teachers

The instructor explains the game and its rules, allowing a brief time for practice and explanation of the scoring. After explaining the general principles of the game, he leaves to give instructions to those who are waiting in the adjoining room.

Instructions to Those Who Will Take the Role of Failure

(The members of this group have declared that failure has not been a problem. Note the role reversal.)

"All of you are to be failures in playing Tiddly-Winks, a very simple game. You will be awkward, ignorant, shy, and withdrawn, unwilling to practice, unwilling to learn. You will consistently and persistently make protestations that you have never been good at anything. You will be reluctant and resistant to whatever the teacher tries to get you to do. Do not laugh. Be extremely serious. Act gloomy, bored, tired, indifferent, or helpless. Pout, quit, or do whatever you choose to do in order to portray your role of failure. In playing your role try to respond appropriately to the methods of your teacher. Are there any questions?"

Activity

The *students* return to the classroom to play their roles of failure as the *teachers* teach them the game of Tiddly-Winks.

After about fifteen or twenty minutes of play, the leader invites a discussion of the feelings provoked by the exercise.

Questions for Discussion

1. How did the people who were acting as failures feel about their teachers?
2. How did the teachers feel about the failures?
3. What is the impact on others of a person who frequently expresses his attitude of failure?

4. How does a person feel when he is attempting to help someone who declares he is a failure or exhibits an attitude of failure?

Response of the Pilot Group: Quotations

How the Failures Felt about the Teachers

"The teacher's enthusiasm dwindled rapidly."

"They kept trying to push us to do things we didn't want to do."

"Some were encouraging at the beginning, but they felt apathy and disgust at the end."

"Some of the teachers covered up their hostility by laughing."

"Teachers saw the set-up right away, and some did not participate."

How the Teachers Felt While Dealing with the Failures

"I felt double-crossed."

"I felt frustrated."

"I felt angry."

"I felt they were not trying."

"I felt impatient."

"I quit trying to teach them."

"I felt like a failure myself."

"I was disgusted."

"I was amused because it was just play-acting."

Section IV

Exploring the Boundaries of the Self

UNIT I—UNIVERSALITY, COMMONALITY AND SINGULARITY

SESSION 1—LIKE ALL MEN, LIKE SOME MEN, LIKE NO MAN

> Every man is in certain respects like all other men, like some other men, like no other man.[1]

Theoretical Presentation

DIFFERENCES AND SIMILARITIES between people are the stuff of which human relationships are made. In order to understand ourselves, we must become aware of those aspects of being which we share with all other human beings. As we achieve maturity, we find the area of commonality has expanded, and we feel increasingly wider relatedness with all others.

When a person becomes apt in delineating his own personality, he becomes abler in establishing relatedness with those who differ from him. Further, he learns to develop and capitalize on the aspects of his own personality in which his differences from others are most marked. In so doing, he begins to make his own special contribution to his family, his community, his nation, or his world, in keeping with his special talents. Achievements that are specific to individual talents yield both a sense of accomplishment and fulfillment and the possibility of economic reward.

Today our exercise will examine some of the ways in which each person is like all other men, like some other men, and like no other man.

Organization

Each participant works by himself.

Equipment

Pink, green, and red slips of construction paper, about 3 x 9 in.; felt marking pens.

------

[1] Kluckhohn, Clyde and Murray, Henry A. (Eds.): *Personality in Nature, Society and Culture,* 2nd ed. New York, Knopf, 1953.

Instructions

"Write your name on the top right-hand corner of each slip of paper. Hold the paper horizontally. On the pink slips of paper, write those respects in which you are like *all* other men. On the green slips of paper, write those respects in which you are like *some* other men. On the red slips of paper, write those respects in which you are like *no* other man. Write each characteristic on one slip of paper. Do not write combinations of traits, such as *personality*."

Activity

Members of the group fill out the pink, green, and red slips. When all have finished writing, the instructor collects the slips for use in several succeeding periods.

Response of the Pilot Group: Instructor's Observations

The red slips presented the greatest problem. The search for uniqueness was made quite difficult by the ruling that general terms such as *personality* were not to be used. The group found it virtually impossible to find any specific characteristic in which one person differed from all others. Those characteristics mentioned, such as "A scar just below my right ear," "My fingerprints," etc. were of such minute significance that the problem was highlighted. It also became apparent that such items of individuality have little to do with the self or selfhood. The group gradually came to the realization that it is only through a combination of traits that we achieve idiosyncrasy or singularity.

SESSION 2—UNIVERSALITY

Organization

Free movement within the room. Chairs are pushed back against the wall.

Equipment

The pink slips of paper on which each person has previously written those characteristics he has in common with all other men.

Instructions

"For today, this class will represent all men. All members of the human race are included in this room. Wander around the room, talking to each person in turn. Discuss what you have written on your pink slips. If you find someone who does not have the particular trait or characteristic that you have listed as being universal, you are to tear up your pink slip. The trait or characteristic you have written is not universal."

Activity

The participants wander around the room as instructed. After a period that allows participants to talk with most of the people in the group, the participants are asked to reconvene and report on their experiences.

Response of the Pilot Group: Collation

Universality

I am a human being. I have to breathe, eat, and drink to stay alive. I am physically a complete unit. I have body characteristics. I have a brain and a heart. I have feelings and thoughts. I have the power to reason and evaluate. I have experiences I call *good* experiences and experiences I call *bad* experiences.

I am a selfish person. I have my own likes and dislikes. I want things done my way.

I am full of feelings for myself and others. I have experienced a variety of feelings: love, anger, pain, and fear. My feelings can be hurt. I get depressed at times.

I have relationships with others. I need others. I need love. I want to be loved. I feel affection for others and feel lonely without their affection. My relating with others results in my having feelings for and about them and myself. I have feelings of anger when someone attacks me.

I want to be happy and have peace of mind. I want to live life to its fullest as a productive person.

I have a limited life span.

SESSION 3—COMMONALITY

Organization
Chairs are pushed back against the wall. Participants move freely about the room.

Equipment
The green slips of paper on which each person has previously written those characteristics he has in common with *some* other men.

Instructions
"Move around the room and discuss your green slips of paper with the others. As you talk with them, find those persons who have listed similar interests, backgrounds, or traits. Join with them in a group. Form an organization representing your particular traits or interests. Define the goals of your organization. Attempt to recruit members from other groups if you like. Prohibit members with certain traits from joining your group if you wish to discriminate."

Activity
Participants move about the room discussing their slips of paper and forming organizations. When the activity has subsided, participants are asked to sit in their groups and discuss their experiences.

Questions for Discussion
1. How did you behave in this situation?
2. Whom did you join? Why did you select those particular people?
3. What did you notice about the behavior of others in this situation?
4. How did groups deal with other groups?
5. What do men have in common?

SESSION 4—SINGULARITY

Organization

Free movement within the room.

Equipment

Previously written red slips of paper listing those character-istics held in common with *no one else*.

Instructions

"Wander around the room and discuss with others the characteristics on your papers. If you find anyone who has the same item on his paper that you have on yours, both of you are to tear up your slips of paper and throw them away. That trait or characteristic cannot be unique if someone else has it also."

Activity

Participants confront each other with the red slips as indicated in the instructions. After a sufficient time for confrontation with most of the people in the room, the participants reconvene for a discussion.

The leader conducts a discussion on the ways in which human beings are unique. Participants are invited to comment upon significant experiences they had during the period.

Response of the Pilot Group: Collation

Singularity

I am not like anyone else in this room. I have a unique set of genes that determine my character traits and physical appear-ance. No one else has the exact facial characteristics that I possess. No other man smiles showing his dimples, teeth, and eyes exactly as I do. No one else has the exact number of freckles that I have. No one else has a mole on his left little toe. My eyesight is not like that of others. I am different from

----

NOTE: This lesson is designed to confront participants with the fact that their personality traits are not as different from others as their thinking had led them to believe. The confrontation may well produce anger.

anyone else in this room because I have a birthmark on my right thigh.

I have had a set of experiences that no one else has had. No one else in this room is from Mineral Wells, Texas. I was a petty officer in the Navy in 1932 and hated it. I am different from all others in my exact degree of knowledge. I am trying to raise Appaloosa horses. I can speak Chinese. I am not like anyone in this room because when someone sneezes I say the old saying, "Scat, kitty cat, your tail is in the gravy." No one else has the exact tastes I have in houses, dogs, food, clothes, music or make-up. I am different from all others in the rate of time and the efficiency with which I accomplish certain tasks.

No one else has the same family I have. No other person has my feelings or reactions to my mate, or my love for my children. I have a distinct set of feelings and thoughts. I am acutely aware of my needs within myself. I am always serious about myself. Only I can really understand and know myself.

UNIT II—LIFE SPACE

SESSION 1—WHAT IS LIFE SPACE?[1]

Theoretical Presentation

Each person has a certain space, both physical and psychological, which he occupies. Within this area, however spacious or confining, he exists and exercises the prerogatives of his own individuality. Once outside his own area, he then moves on communal ground, where the rights of others must be considered and where adaptation becomes necessary. Occasionally he is predator in a third area where he encroaches upon the spatial rights of others or where he infringes on the intimate life space of another person.

The biological base for the spatial existence for each individual is emphasized in *The Territorial Imperative*.[2] Ardrey demonstrates that each species of animal has its own territory in which it exists and lives and which it defends from attack by other species. Ardrey views this territorial concept as the basis of human morality.

> And finally we must know that the territorial imperative—just one, it is true, of the evolutionary forces playing upon our lives—is the biological law on which we have founded our edifices of human morality. Our capacities for sacrifice, for altruism, for sympathy, for trust, for responsibilities to other than self-interest, for honesty, for charity, for friendship and love, for social amity and mutual interdependence have evolved just as surely as the flatness of our feet, the muscularity of our buttocks, and the enlargement of

---

NOTE: The concept of life space provides the components for establishing reasonable self-assertion. This is a lecture only, followed by a discussion of the lecture.

[1] The concept of life space is credited to Kurt Lewin. Lewin, Kurt: *A Dynamic Theory of Personality, Selected Papers of Kurt Lewin*. New York, McGraw, 1935. Lewin, Kurt: *Resolving Social Conflicts*. New York, Harper, 1948.

[2] Ardrey, Robert: *The Territorial Imperative*. New York, Atheneum, 1966.

our brains, out of the encounter on ancient African savannahs between the primate potential and the hominid circumstances. Whether morality without territory is possible in man must remain our final unanswerable question.[3]

In our culture, when finances allow, a new baby receives his own room. He is given his own clothes, toys, furniture, etc., all of which become incorporated as part of the life space he gradually learns to defend. Common areas in private homes are usually kitchens, bathrooms and living rooms. Spatial rights come into jeopardy and cause contention whenever individuals attempt to dominate common areas or control the use of common equipment. Familiar in every family are controversies over the use of television, telephone, and bathroom. Time use, space use, and equipment use become sources of differences and argument; and if encroachment is to be avoided, one must defend his own spatial rights and recognize the rights of others.

Spatial rights are further enforced in our culture by means of individual ownership of land and property, and our entire legal structure is designed to protect these rights and to protect the individual from infringement of his rights to such ownership. Our concept of life-space for each person extends beyond death when the deceased is accorded a coffin and cemetery or mausoleum space defined in perpetuity.

If an individual is to be able to enjoy a sense of freedom in his life processes, he must become aware of that which he believes to be his proper space; he must learn to defend himself from infringement upon his own life space, to recognize common ground, and to beware of infringement upon the life space of others. Every person has a responsibility to defend that which is within the confines of his own space, but he must avoid a desire for sole control over that space which he shares with others or control over areas which rightfully are within the space of others.

Through communication a person learns to define his own space, to share common areas with others, and to hear the communications of others which warn of infringement and trespass.

---

[3] Ardrey, *op. cit.*, p. 351.

Activity

For the remainder of the period, a discussion is conducted on the concept of life space. The instructor concludes the period with a reading of the following quotation:

Reading

. . . The night may be no less dark, the stars no less distant, the human outcome no less uncertain, the voices that advise us in forgotten tongues no less incomprehensible. But we have made a little place in the forest that we may regard as our own. We have sniffed about, recognized a few of its potential resources, found a hiding place or two that seem secure. We have marked out as well as we could the boundaries of our new domain and deposited scent on this tree trunk, that bush, to inform intruders that someone is home. We are predators, of course, and from time to time we shall go out looting and raping and raising general havoc in the surrounding countryside. There will be reprisals, naturally. And that is another reason why it will be good to have some place to stand, some place to regard as ours.[4]

It is a matter of surpassing remark, when you come down to think about it, what a change in the landscape occurs when you have made a place of your own! how the shape of an oak tree emerges in the darkness to take on that definition which can only be oak; how stars shine brighter, and those of fifth or even sixth magnitude become apparent; how the sound of some running brook— it must be a long way off—chants, its quiet cadence; how smells rush at you, the smell of mint—could it be from the brook? impossible— the smell of leaves, green leaves dampened by dew, but of other leaves also, old leaves, last year's fallen leaves, that sweet, soft odor of death's decomposition. And then there is that muskiness. There is an animal somewhere.[5]

---

[4] Ardrey, *op cit.*, p. 352.
[5] *Ibid.*, p. 353.

SESSION 2—DELINEATION OF LIFE SPACE

Organization
All furniture is cleared from the room, leaving only bare floor.

Equipment
Red papers, representing singularity, from a previous session; a large ball of string.

Instructions
"Enclose your life space with a piece of string. You may make the space any size or shape you wish it to be. On the floor inside your space put your red papers from the previous unit on Singularity. These papers list the ways in which you are unique.

"Try to keep others from infringing on your space or taking your red papers. Accept responsibility for protecting your space and the red papers that are in it. You can defend your space and your papers only when you yourself are in your space. It is not possible to defend from a distance, while you are in someone else's space, or when you are on common ground.

"If you are asked to defend someone else's space or to protect his individuality, do not do so. That is his responsibility. Do not concern yourself in any way with another person's space; it is not your problem if *he* abnegates *his* responsibilities.

"You may, however, try to acquire another's space and acquire another's red papers."

Activity
Participants break off pieces of string and establish their desired life spaces. Each places his red slips of paper within his space and each defends his space as he chooses.

After fifteen or twenty minutes of interaction, the instructor reconvenes the class and conducts a discussion.

Questions for Discussion
1. What characterized the shape of your life space? The shape of others' life spaces?

NOTE: This session is wild and interesting, provocative of individualized responses. The instructor should function as observer, since participants are too involved in their own actions to see what is going on with others.

2. What observations did you make about the size of your life space as compared to others?
3. Describe the role you assumed in defending your life space.
4. Describe your role in relation to attack on the spaces of others.
5. Was anyone completely dispossessed? If so, explain what happened.

Response of the Pilot Group: Instructor's Observations

Roles in the Establishment of Life Space

The Spaceless. Some members refused to participate to the extent of defining a space for themselves. Instead, they wandered about, watching others.

The Passive. Some defined their spaces in remote parts of the room or beneath the portable chalkboard where they would not be easily accessible to others.

The Overdefender. Some stationed themselves in corners with their backs to the wall, where it would not be necessary to defend on all sides.

The Sooner. Some rushed to establish a large space in advance of others and continued to defend it throughout the period.

The Negotiator. Some established peace pacts with those in contiguous spaces.

The Womb Inhabitant. One member established his space within the confines of another's space.

The Commune. A few members established a joint space which they maintained in a communal manner.

Roles in Response to Attacks on Life Space

The Homeless. Some lost their space to attackers and were never able to reestablish another space. They wandered hopelessly and became totally nonparticipating.

The Predator. Some members, after losing their spaces, abandoned any attempt to establish a new life space and devoted their entire attention to attacks on the spaces of others.

The Voyager. Some moved their spaces to a new site each time they were attacked.

The Accommodator. Some changed their boundaries, yielding

a certain amount of their space to another, while the attacker yielded some space to them.

The Fortifier. Some barricaded their areas with walls and with their bodies.

The Pugilist. Some fought off all intruders with physical violence.

SESSION 3—FEELINGS ABOUT LIFE SPACE

Organization

Regular classroom seating. Each participant works by himself at his seat.

Equipment

Pencil and paper for each person.

Instructions

"Write your answers to the questions, with each answer on a separate piece of paper. Put your name on each of the papers."

Activity

Participants write answers to the questions. When writing is finished, the instructor collects the papers. Before the next period, the answers are collated, to be used as a basis for discussion.

Questions for Written Answers

1. What is life space?
2. How do you acquire life space?
3. What do you do with life space when you have it?
4. How do you feel when you don't have any life space? How do you feel when you have life space?
5. How is life space related to maturity?

Response of the Pilot Group: Collation

What Is Life Space?

Life space is a notion of the self, of the psyche's inviolate territory. Life space is a construct created to name my intangible responsibility to myself to know how to live and to adjust to an ever-changing daily life.

Life space is a psychiatric concept of the boundaries of a person's likes and dislikes, interests, beliefs, activities, thoughts, and goals.

Life space is my personal frame of reference, including all

NOTE: This session is devoted to writing of and discussing the activity in the previous session. Additional class sessions may be needed to complete the discussion of life space, since it is a very basic concept.

action and ideas; it is an idea of what I have a right to want, anticipate, expect, and strive for.

Life space is the natural area in which I as a person live, work, and play; it is the territory across which I reach to gain contact with associates in work, social life, and family life.

My life space may be large or small and may be in various shapes. It is not of fixed size but is changing constantly, depending on my own activities.

How Do You Acquire Life Space?

I acquire life space by taking responsibility for myself and my actions, by defending my right to have it.

I acquire life space through self-exploration of my talents and abilities; it is acquired by knowing myself. As strengths and weaknesses are recognized, if I wish to grow I will begin to define for myself the areas and boundaries of my life space.

Life space is acquired through birth, kept through determination, and lost through weakness in the face of the predator.

What Do You Do When You Have Life Space?

When I have life space, I either occupy it or lose it. Life space is mine to protect and, when necessary, to defend.

People will try to take away my life space, either consciously or unconsciously.

I defend it when necessary, share it when desired, expand it, define it, develop it, and live in it.

I use it to promote my specific interests and needs. When I have too much life space, I will fail or be overworked. I will then lose space I cannot take care of.

How Do You Feel When You Have Life Space?

Life space can be a delightful possession which pleases, a tiresome chore which irritates or confuses, a difficult goal which causes exhaustion in attaining, or a thing which is taken for granted and causes no noticeable emotion.

When I have life space, I feel a purpose in life: self-confident, assured, secure, content, self-satisfied, well-adjusted, full, responsible, self-controlled, powerful, and aware.

How Do You Feel When You Don't Have Any Life Space?

I cannot be aware of something I have never had and do not have. Without life space, a person who is not aware of lacking it may feel "used" by others, lost in the middle of people and generally helpless. Life doesn't mean much, for I live in a void. I have no identity because I have not earned it.

I feel defeated, depressed, unworthy, inadequate as a person, frustrated, insecure, completely unnecessary, lost, dejected, unstable, restricted, desolate, lonely, and without purpose.

Life space may be small, but it depends entirely on a person's needs, wants, and philosophy as to whether it is lonely or restricted to him.

How Is Life Space Related to Maturity?

Maturity is directly proportional to the awareness of life space, its complete occupancy and its correct usage. A mature person fills his life space continuously and consistently, with adequacy and self-esteem.

A mature person does not allow others to intrude on or invade his life space. He recognizes his rights and defends his beliefs.

A mature person is aware of and respects the life space of others. He is capable of occupying his own life space without intruding on others. If his grasp hinders others' life spaces, the balance of maturity is lost.

UNIT III—DIMENSIONS OF THE SELF

SESSION 1—THE SELF-GRAPH: PUNCTUALITY

Organization

REGULAR CLASSROOM SEATING.

Equipment

Graph paper, pencils, paper.

Instructions

"Today you will make a bar graph of yourself. Divide your paper into three vertical sections. Underneath the first section write *Punctuality;* under the second, *Neatness;* under the third, *Patience.*

"If the bottom of the paper represents zero percent and the top of the paper represents one hundred percent, fill in a bar for each quality to show the percentage you have of that quality."

Activity

Members of the group prepare their bar graphs. When the graphs are completed, the group is ready for the next part of the activity.

Instructions

"We will start with punctuality. Try to find someone else in the group who is your exact opposite—in other words, if your graph represents sixty percent, the graph of the person you find should represent forty percent. Your combined scores on punctuality should be as close to one hundred percent as possible. When you have paired with an opposite, join together with two or three other pairs, to make groups of six or eight. Each group should have as many persons who are low as it has persons who are high on this trait.

"Decide on a name for your group, since we will keep these same groups for several sessions. Select a recorder. In your groups, explore how each of you feels about punctuality. What is the difference between those who are high on this trait and those who are low? The recorder should write your conclusions on the papers I have given you."

Activity

Groups meet and discuss punctuality for fifteen or twenty minutes.

Instructions

"We are now ready to hear the report from the recorder of each group. Group I, what is your group's name? Let us have your report."

Activity

The leader calls upon the recorder of each group, asking for its name first. After the reports are concluded, participants are told to keep their same groups for the next session.

Response of the Pilot Group: Quotations

Those high on punctuality . . .

"Waste time being early for appointments."

"Always punctual. Don't like to be late."

"Hate to wait for others. Detest people who are late, especially if they never try to be on time."

"Don't mind waiting for a doctor."

"Feel there are few excuses for being late."

"Like children home on time."

"Like the milkman to be on time."

"Do not like long phone conversations."

"Feel lateness is rude for dinners, appointments, or any event which has a speaker."

"Feel people must have a good excuse if they are late."

Those low on punctuality . . .

"Are late if going to something they don't like."

"Don't mind if others are late."

"Stay in bed as long as they can."
"Do not put a time structure on daily activities."
"Don't mind waiting a reasonable time."
"Flexible with self and others about time."

Summary

"Those who are high on the graph, for the most part, have rigid time structures for themselves and for others. These people get more angry at themselves than at others for lateness.

"Those low on the graph have more relaxed attitudes toward punctuality for themselves and others."

SESSION 2—NEATNESS

Organization
Members resume grouping of the previous period.

Equipment
Self-graphs from the last period, writing paper, pencils.

Instructions
"Today we will discuss neatness. Select a different recorder from the one you had yesterday. The recorder will write the conclusions of the group discussion and report at the end of the period.

"How do you feel about neatness? What is the difference in the feelings of those who rated themselves high on this trait and those who rated themselves low? Is there a correlation between individual feelings about punctuality and feelings about neatness?"

Activity
Groups meet and discuss neatness for twenty or thirty minutes.

Instructions
"Now let us hear from the recorder of each group. Group I, what is your name, and what have you to report?"

Activity
Reports are made by the recorder of each group, in turn.

Response of the Pilot Group: Collation
People are either very neat or very messy. There are more sloppy people than neat people.

Messy people are upsetting in their home. It bothers messy people when they can't find their belongings.

Neat people believe in a place for everything and everything in its place. Sometimes people are neat only because they are scared of what others will say.

A neat person wants others to be the same way. Neat people are upset by other people who upset the neatness they have created.

Neat people are bothered by drawers left open; lids un-screwed; beds unmade; towels left lying around in the bathroom after use; half-filled glasses and cups; messy or cluttered drawers and shelves; messy bathrooms.

Neat people like books in bookcase alphabetized; clothes in closet organized as to type, hanging neatly and all facing the same direction; everything compartmentalized; worn or tattered clothes disposed of; things lined up; beds made; ashtrays clean; pillows arranged in a certain way; towels folded in a particular way; even hems; perfectly fitting clothes; hair in place all the time; make-up just so; paper that is smooth, clean, and without crumpled corners; bottles and medicines arranged in order by size and according to frequency of usage; trash emptied at all times; kitchen spotlessly clean.

Neat people are also punctual.

SESSION 3—PATIENCE

Organization

Members are in the same groups as for the previous sessions.

Equipment

Self-graphs from Section IV, Unit II, Session 1; writing paper, and pencils.

Instructions

"Today let us discuss patience. Select a different recorder from the one you had yesterday. The recorder will write the conclusions of the group discussion and report at the end of the period. How much patience have you? What is the difference between those who rated themselves high on patience and those who rated themselves low on patience? Is patience related to punctuality and neatness? How much patience is too little? Too much? How do you feel when you have too little patience? How do you feel when you have too much patience?"

Activity

Groups meet and discuss patience for twenty or thirty minutes.

Instructions

"Let us now hear from the recorder for each group."

Activity

Recorders from each group give oral reports and turn in written reports.

Response of the Pilot Group: Collation

Patience is too little . . .

When you jump to conclusions without thinking.

When you are not tolerant of others' shortcomings.

When you can't conduct yourself in a reasonable and proper manner.

When you end up with results you did not intend.

When you cut off communication.

When you make others feel inferior.

When you make others feel afraid.
When you make others feel uneasy and on guard.
When you explode.
Patience is too much . . .
When you deprive others of responsibility.
When you give others a false sense of your values.
When you confuse yourself as to how you feel.
When you make others feel inferior or superior.
When you act patient but do not feel it.
When your patience is abused by others.
When you lose your sense of identity.
When you feel constrained.
When you are angry because you are more patient than you want to be.
When you become afraid of other people.
When you are afraid you won't be liked.
When you merely tolerate others.
When you are self-critical.

Summary

When you have too little patience, you feel frustrated, angry, and guilty.

When you have too much patience, you feel frustrated, angry, and resentful.

SESSION 4—MONEY

Prior Preparation Required

Preceding the session, participants should have been asked to bring to class some item of personal property which they do not mind selling. An appropriate limitation can be put on its value—for example, an item which the participant would be willing to sell for a price between $.50 and $2.00. It should be made clear that this is not to be a junk item nor one of excessive value.

Theoretical Presentation

Since the use of money is crucial in human interaction, a study of attitudes toward money can contribute much in the delineation of the self. By examining our attitudes toward money —and our use of it—we can learn much about ourselves.

We tend to think of money as being purely material, unrelated to the emotions. Nothing could be farther from fact. Money is probably the most emotionally laden aspect of living. Through the use of money, we express the entire gamut of emotions. Through the ways we deal with money, we manifest many personality traits. Yet, despite its emotionally laden qualities, we all recognize that in itself, money contributes little overall happiness beyond its ability to buy the basic necessities for life and health.

Organization

The groups from the previous period may be used, or the group may be redivided by random selection. Sale items should not be revealed until the group division is completed. Groups are seated around tables.

Equipment

Play money in small denominations, an amount sufficient to give each group enough to buy about half of the total items brought by participants; items brought for sale. (Participants who have not bothered to bring an item are not allowed to participate.)

Instructions

"In each group, display your sale items on the tables. I have given each group twenty dollars.

"You may sell your items at any price you wish.

"In each group, gather around your table and determine the selling price for each item you have for sale. You may have fixed prices or you may bargain. You may post prices if you wish, or you may have the prices only in the minds of the members of your group. You may alter the prices on items at any time you wish—either up or down.

"Now meet in your groups and decide on the prices you wish to charge for your items."

Activity

Groups meet around the tables and price the items the members have brought for sale.

Instructions

"Put your group's items on the table for display. Now go around to each of the other groups and see what they have for sale. Do not buy anything yet. Simply look over the market."

Activity

Members of the class wander about and inspect the items for sale at the other tables.

Instructions

"Now, reconvene in your original groups. You have about five minutes to make plans for buying and selling your merchandise. You may delegate the various responsibilities as you wish and spend your group money in any way you decide."

Activity

Groups meet and discuss plans for buying and selling.

Instructions

"The Trade Fair is now open. You may buy and sell."

Activity

The buying and selling period continues for twenty minutes or until interest has subsided, whichever is sooner.

Instructions

"The Trade Fair is now closed. Reconvene in your groups and discuss the results of your experiences. How did your group handle the buying and selling? Was the way you spent money related to your personality? How did the compulsive people differ in behavior from impulsive people."

Activity

Groups conduct a discussion. When the entire group reconvenes, the important points of the discussion are written on the board.

Response of the Pilot Group

Instructor's Observations

One of the groups ended up with over half of the total amount of money issued to the class. This group was competitive and enthusiastic at the outset and in the end had a vicious desire to sell at a profit and obtain more and more money. This they accomplished successfully by refusing to pay the prices asked by the other groups, by selling their own items for high prices and reselling at profitable prices items bought from other groups.

A few individuals paid ridiculously high prices for certain items. Some participants were more interested in buying and some more interested in selling. Some would not sell at all.

Conclusions

Money is an emotionally loaded subject.

Spenders irritate savers. Savers irritate spenders.

Many people are inconsistent, being extravagant in small items but hesitant to spend money on large items, or vice versa.

Many people are hostile, competitive, and uncooperative in the area of money.

Apportioning certain amounts of money to individuals in a group is a method often used to allow individual freedom in expenditure, but it does not lead to a resolution of conflicts in the area of money.

It is best to be neither a spendthrift nor a miser.

SESSION 5—PROTOTYPE OF THE COMPULSIVE PERSONALITY AND MAXIMS FOR MITIGATION

"The work of the world is done by compulsive people."[1]

Theoretical Presentation

Compulsive people derive satisfaction from the process of creating order. Their energy may be expended in organizing abstract knowledge, material things, or live people. Since compulsive people comprise the productive group, without them human civilization would not have developed to its present state.

Being a compulsive person has both advantages and disadvantages. If one is compulsive, he has the potential for being a very productive person, but excessive compulsiveness may lead to psychiatric hospitalization. Let us examine today the advantages and disadvantages inherent in being a compulsive person, and let us then determine what can be done to augment the advantages and minimize or mitigate the disadvantages.

Questions for Discussion

1. What traits or attributes do compulsive people have?
2. What kinds of professions or trades utilize these attributes to advantage?
3. What kinds of recreation do compulsive people choose?
4. What kinds of difficulties with themselves do compulsive people encounter?
5. What kinds of difficulties do compulsive people have with others?

Response of the Pilot Group: Collation

Compulsive people are perfectionistic, exacting, methodical, neat, clean, orderly, punctual, precise, rigid, time-conscious, self-controlled, self-disciplined, patient.

Compulsiveness enhances success in many fields. A compulsive person with appropriate qualifications would be effective as a bookkeeper, musician, engineer, mathematician, scientist, elec-

---

[1] Statement by Charles L. Bloss, M.D., Timberlawn Psychiatric Hospital, Dallas, Texas.

trician, banker, housemaid, secretary, taxidermist, teacher, military strategist, laboratory technician, beautician, computer programmer, carpenter, horticulturist, nurse, doctor, ticket agent, jeweller, pilot, astronaut, librarian, recreation therapist.

Compulsive people have difficulty with themselves in the following ways: They seek escape from self-imposed pressures through alcoholism, dope addiction, depression, suicide, and murder; they are inefficient because of furtive efforts to escape self-imposed dilemmas; they are angry with themselves when they do not produce as they think they should; they are frustrated when routines are interrupted; they ambivalate between superiority and inferiority; they are afraid of their aloneness.

Compulsive people have difficulty with others in the following ways: They are jealous; they are impatient with others who do not conform to their standards and produce as they think the others should produce; they are dominating down to the specific detail; they always want to be in control.

For recreation, compulsive people make their hobbies into work; they like reading, collecting, organizing, and competitive activities. Many seek escape in drinking and gambling.

Instructor's Summary

Maxims for Mitigation of Compulsiveness

1. Define your compulsive personality as exactly as possible. Explore the exact limits of each compulsive trait: How, where, when, and in what manner is each portion of compulsiveness expressed?

2. To those you live with, try to express verbally all of your specific tastes and preferences related to daily living patterns. If you like your egg cooked for exactly two minutes and served with its large end up and in a blue and white egg cup, say so. If your pepper must be freshly ground, if you use only artificial salt, say so.

3. Indulge in extremes of compulsiveness during leisure time and hobby activities. Ride a ten-speed bicycle, jog, figure skate, play chess, collect stamps, classify butterflies, or participate in one or more similarly compulsive hobbies.

4. Enter competitions extensively and freely; search for opponents who are more skillful than you.

5. Select a highly compulsive type of work which challenges your compulsiveness to the fullest extent, yet still allows for sufficient contact with people to mitigate loneliness.

6. Enclose and limit your responsibilities. Resist or cast off global concerns and overextended, colossal organizational tasks. If you must assume extended responsibilities, share them with others. Apportion your tasks among those concerned.

7. Decide which of your idiosyncrasies you enjoy and which you would prefer to rid yourself of. Take steps to eliminate those you do not wish to have.

8. If you are compulsive, you probably have explosive areas. Try to modify these areas so that the explosiveness is not too costly. For instance, if your problem is ambivalence between impulsive spending and miserly saving, patronize second-hand stores and garage sales where it is possible to enjoy the process of impulsive buying without spending too much.

9. Avoid the seduction of dramatic and melodramatic situations in your efforts to relieve loneliness. Avoid difficulties and complications whenever possible. Attempt to achieve simplicity.

10. Ask for and consider the opinions of others in order to check out your own reality perception.

11. Try to solve problems in the here and now. Instead of searching for a new place, a new time, and new friends, look for problem solutions in alteration and modification of present situations.

UNIT IV—THRESHOLDS OF THE SELF

SESSION 1—MY NAME IS...

There is my name, my representative force in the hearing of those who make up my world, my sound effect, my story and my theme song, my personal share in the moving history that has made this land.[1]

Theoretical Presentation

THROUGHOUT THE AGES men have believed, as we still believe, that names have magic—that the name is the symbol of the person, the symbol of the self, and the symbol of identity.

> In certain countries your name was your secret, never to be spoken before strangers lest some enemy use it to do you harm, while in other lands your name was so secret it could not even be spoken by your own father and mother. In ancient Egypt one's name was a separate entity with a life of its own, and even in Rome a name was well-guarded lest it be used by the unfriendly for black magic. The Chinese gave their babies unpleasant names that would not tempt the envy of the gods. With the same hope of protection, parents in other lands named their babies for the pagan gods, mighty heroes, powerful animals, and, eventually, for saints.[2]

We enjoy having our name on our mailbox, our parking place, our towel, our welcome mat. We like initials on jewelry, handbags, wallets, sweaters, or license plates. We have become the person who has our name. Let us examine that name.

Organization

A circle or double circle arrangement that will encourage discussion.

Equipment

Paper, pencil and crayons for each participant.

NOTE: Discussion of names can extend several sessions.

[1] Wells, Evelyn: *What to Name the Baby: A Treasury of Names*. Garden City, Garden City Books, 1953, p. 3.

[2] *Ibid.*, p. 5.

Instructions

"Write your name on the paper. Write it several different ways. Print it. Make it very small, then very large. Misspell it. Change it by adding or omitting a letter. Color your name. Decorate it in some way. Say it loudly. Whisper it. Sing it. Tell your neighbors your name. Ask your neighbors their names. Talk about your names."

Activity

Participants follow the directions. When the activity has subsided, the leader conducts a discussion.

Questions for Discussion

1. What is the origin of your name?[3]
   Animal: Bear, Lion, Wolf
   Personal characteristic: Hardy, Longfellow, Hale, Short
   Natural phenomenon: Wind, Storm
   Occupation: Miller, Fowler, Forester, Weaver, Smith
   Place: Craig (crag), Bradley (from the broad lea), Halford (from the hall by the ford)
   Pageantry: Pope, Page, Abbot, Baron, Squire
   Color: Russet, White, Brown, Black
   Jewels: Garnet, Ruby, Diamond
   Son of: Johnson, Stephenson
2. How do you sign your name? Do you sign your full name, including your middle name? What part do you eliminate? Under what circumstances?
3. Did your parents have something specific in mind when they named you? What?
4. How do you feel about your name? What feelings does it evoke in you?
5. Does your name have a sex? Is the sex of your name the same as yours?
6. Do you wear monograms? Do you have your name on your house? Your stationery? Your cigarette lighter? Do you like this? Why do you do it?

---

[3] Wells, *op. cit.*, p. 6.

7. How does your name seem when you sign it on a check? On a petition? On a birth certificate? On an application for a loan? On a legal contract? On your will?

8. How would you prefer to have your name written on your tombstone?

9. Have you ever changed your name? What was it before you changed it? Why did you change it? Has your family changed its name?

10. If you are a married woman, did you have feelings about changing your name and taking your husband's name? If you are a man, how did you feel when your wife took your name?

11. If you could change your name to anything you wanted, what would you name yourself?

12. Do you have a nickname? Do you like nicknames? Do others call you by a nickname? Who? Under what circumstances? Do you call others by a nickname? Who? Under what circumstances?

13. Do you have pet names for people? Do other people call you pet names? Do you like to be called pet names?

14. How do you feel when someone forgets your name? Misspells it? Mispronounces it?

15. How well do you remember the names of others? Whose names do you forget? Why do you remember some names and why do you forget other names?

16. Under what circumstances do you try to be anonymous? Do you like being nameless? What are you hiding when you don't use your name?

17. Is there anything ridiculous about your name? Your initials?

18. How do you communicate with names? Urgency? Emphasis? Approval? Disapproval?

19. Did your parents use your name differently under different circumstances? How? In what situations?

20. Do you express anger in the way you use names?

21. How do you use names when you want something?

22. Is there anything else you express through the use of names?

SESSION 2—THE GROUP GRAPH

Theoretical Presentation

One of the ways in which we learn to delineate ourselves is by comparing ourselves to others. All of us spend a considerable portion of our time making comparisons, but few of us care to admit that we do so. Nor do we like to acknowledge the conclusions we reach.

Since comparison is inevitable, it would be well to learn to use it constructively. Comparison can contribute vastly to self-knowledge. Those qualities we admire in others and those we resent in others are often reflections of our own values. By examining our attitudes toward others, we can gain insights into our own behavior.

Comparison may also serve to increase one's sense of commonality. The more mature a person becomes, the more he recognizes what he has in common with others. At the same time, he becomes more aware of that within him which is unique or unusual.

Organization

The room is arranged so that it is possible for all members of the group to stand in a single line. The line can be either straight or curved, but the sequential relationship between each person in line should be clear.

Equipment

One sign which says *0* and one sign which says *100*. At one end of the line the *0* sign is placed; at the other end, the *100* sign.

Instructions

"Line up in a single file, with one end of the line here and the other end of the line there. You should be in a single file, facing toward me. This line represents a human graph or scale, ranging from *0* at one end to *100* at the other. I will read to you a series of characteristics. If you believe you have a higher amount of this characteristic than anyone else in this group, line up at the end marked *100*. If you have the least of this characteristic of anyone else in the group, line up at the *0* end of the scale. You may talk with other people in the class as much as is necessary to determine where you should stand in the line. Do not decide by yourself. You are to discuss at length if necessary. We will practice on the first one. The first one is *Age*."

Activity

Members of the group discuss their ages with each other, and line up accordingly, with the oldest at the *100* end of the scale, and the youngest at the *0* end of the scale.

Instructions

"The next characteristic is blondness. Line up according to degree of blondness."

Activity

Members of the group confer with each other, and line up with the blondest person near the *100* end of the scale and the least blond person near the *0* end of the scale.

Response of the Pilot Group: Instructor's Observations

Confusion begins immediately, since there arise the problems of those who are artificially blond, those who are red-headed, and those who question the degree of blondness in gray hair.

Activity

The instructor proceeds with a list of characteristics, each of which is less definitive and more abstract than the one preceding it. Additional discussion and confusion are to be anticipated.

The qualities listed should apply to the concerns and interests of the members of the group. The following list was used in the pilot class:

1. Degree of illness.
2. Generosity.
3. Kindness.
4. Honesty.
5. Success.

When the exercise is completed, participants discuss their responses.

Questions for Discussion
1. How did you decide where to stand in the line?
2. How could you tell who was sicker, more generous, more kind, etc.?
3. How did you feel when you were at the top of the scale?
4. How did you feel when you were at the bottom of the scale?
5. Why do we compare ourselves with others?
6. What is accomplished by such comparisons?

Response of the Pilot Group: Instructor's Observations

It was necessary for participants to communicate with each other in order to establish their appropriate places in the line. As the characteristics became more abstract, it was apparent that comparisons were often made in the absence of facts and were based on invalid assumptions.

SESSION 3—SELF-PRESENTATION

Prior Preparation Required

At the close of the previous session, the following assignment is made: "Before the next period, make a chart about yourself. Here are sheets of manila tagboard and some marking pens.

"Select some item of information about your personality, your character or your feelings that you would like to communicate or explain to the class through a chart. First, jot down the purpose of your presentation and the main points you want to put across. Using the felt-tipped pen, make a chart or diagram that could be seen from any part of the room. Focus on one principal point about yourself. Each chart should have a simple declarative sentence or key words by way of title or explanation. Members of the audience should be able to read the entire chart in less than a minute without moving from their seats. Avoid detail. Bring your completed charts to the next class session. Remember to bring your felt-tipped pens."

Equipment Given Out at the Previous Session

Manila tagboard sheets, 12 x 18 in.; felt-tipped pens.

Organization

Regular classroom seating.

Equipment

A stopwatch or other timing device.

Instructions

"Each of you in turn will present your chart to the class. Tell briefly what it shows. Make any necessary explanatory comment. If you wish, you may ask questions of the group to make sure they have understood your explanation. Members of the group may also ask questions if the presentations are not clear.

"We will allow two minutes for each presentation and three minutes for discussion. If a speaker takes more than two minutes

_____

NOTE: If this exercise is used, sufficient sessions should be allowed to provide each participant with an opportunity to present his own chart. The exercise is interesting, self-revelatory and time-consuming.

in presentation, less time will be allowed for discussion, up to a total of five minutes. We will need a volunteer to keep time with the stopwatch."

Activity

Individual presentations are made and continued until each person has had an opportunity to present his chart. Regardless of the number of periods involved, each class period concludes with a summary of salient points made during the presentations.

SESSION 4—THE TRANSPARENCY PROMENADE

Theoretical Presentation

As most of you know, dancing was once considered sinful. In order to have a social event which would allow for intermingling of men and women and yet still not sanction dancing, the activity was called a *Promenade*. Instead of dancing, men selected partners for an organized walk. A conversational topic was announced, and each man instructed to discuss this topic with his lady during the *promenade*. Thus today we often refer to dances as *proms*.

Aside from avoiding sin, the promenade provided young men and women with the opportunity to become acquainted by exchanging ideas and exploring a wide variety of concepts. It was, in fact, an organized opportunity for young people to make themselves transparent to some degree: they were asked to offer their ideas, feelings, attitudes, and opinions to others.

In class today we are going to simulate one of these old-fashioned promenades. Since we are exploring the topic of self, I am calling it *The Transparency Promenade*. During the discussion of the topic you may tell as little or as much about yourself as you wish; however, you should not be deceptive. You may avoid or withhold, but you should not lie. Try to make what you do say as truly revealing as is possible.

Organization

The area is cleared of furniture, or the group is moved to a hallway or another empty area. The class is divided into couples, who form into a double circle, facing counterclockwise in the usual *promenade* position familiar in square dances, but not holding hands.

Equipment

A record player and some dance records with moderate tempo, suitable for relaxed walking.

A series of large cards on which are written numbered topics

NOTE: This session is light and enjoyable. It facilitates communication and reaches those who find talking difficult.

for discussion. The cards are numbered consecutively. The following topics suggest the type suitable for the promenade:

1. How I feel about air travel.
2. The people who make up my family group.
3. What I like to read.
4. Music I like and dislike.
5. My favorite dinner menu.
6. Movies I enjoy.
7. How I keep my closet.
8. What I would buy if I had 50 dollars to spend on anything I wanted.
9. An ideal vacation.
10. My dream house.

An easel, portable chalkboard or bulletin board to hold the cards.

Instructions

"On this easel, I am going to place one topic for discussion for each promenade. When the music starts, you will walk around the room in pairs. You will discuss with your partner the topic indicated on the card. Do not talk about anything except the topic written on that particular card. When the music stops, acknowledge that you will be leaving your partner by a polite remark, such as 'I have enjoyed talking with you.'

"Those on the outside of the circle will then move forward to the next person on the inside. This person will be your partner for Promenade 2 and Topic 2. When the music stops again, and you have bid your second partner adieu, those on the outside will again move forward and you will have a new partner for Topic 3. We will continue the process until fifteen minutes before the end of the period. At that time, we will reconvene and discuss our experiences."

Activity

The class follows the outlined procedure for the promenade with Topic 1. Instructions are given again for the change of partners when the music is stopped. A new topic is posted for Promenade 2, etc.

Fifteen minutes before the end of the period, the following questions are discussed.

Questions for Discussion

1. Did you find some people easier to talk to than others? What was it that made these people easy to talk to? What was it that made others harder to talk to? Were you able to talk easily or was it hard for you to reveal yourself?
2. What topics seemed easiest for you to talk about? Which were harder?
3. Would you have liked more time on certain topics? Were there some topics on which it was difficult to fill the time? Why?
4. During the promenades, were you more talkative or less talkative than you usually are? To what do you attribute this?
5. How transparent do you want to be?
6. How capable are you of controlling the degree of self-revelation or transparency that you really want?

SESSION 5—THE CONCEALMENT CONTEST

Organization

The classroom space is cleared of chairs and tables so that members of the group have space in which to move freely about the room.

Equipment

Sufficient beans for each person in the class to have ten (kidney beans, pinto beans, lima beans, or any similar bean that is not too small.)

Instructions

"You will each have ten beans. You are to move around the room and talk to various members of the group. You will be attempting to get each person to give you some information about himself, his feelings, attitudes, or ideas. If he is unable to conceal the information you seek, he will have to give you a bean for each revelation. When a person extracts any information from you, you must give him a bean."

Activity

The class proceeds with the exercise for fifteen minutes, or as long as there is considerable activity and exchange of beans. When the activity has subsided, the leader conducts a discussion of the responses to the exercise.

Questions for Discussion

1. How many of you had more beans at the end than at the beginning?
2. How many of you had fewer beans at the end than at the beginning?
3. How many of you have the same number of beans that you had at the beginning but have exchanged beans in the process?
4. How many of you have the same number of beans that you

NOTE: This session, active and provocative, quickly separates the manipulative people from the nonmanipulative people.

had at the beginning, and have exchanged no beans in the process?

5. How many of you took beans from others by some kind of cheating or deception? What kind?
6. If you won beans from others by some kind of cheating or deception, did you feel guilty about it? Did you give any beans back?
7. Were you aggressive in carrying out the exercise?
8. Were you passive in carrying out the exercise?
9. How many of you surprised yourself by your behavior? What was it about your behavior that surprised you?

Response of the Pilot Group

The response was primarily that of amusement, since the predatory behavior of certain members became apparent. Participants suggested that they had used the following devices to induce self-revelation:

Asking misleading questions.
Asking questions on vulnerable subjects.
Persistent interrogation.
Asking indirect questions.
Asking the question with pseudoinnocence.
Catching people off-guard when they were doing something else.

Participants suggested that they had used the following devices to avoid self-revelation:

Generalizing.
Answering incoherently.
Answering irrelevantly.
Reflecting the question.
Changing the subject.
Claiming a failing memory.
Feigning ignorance.
Pleading the Fifth Amendment.
Pretending deafness.
Making a meaningless exclamation.
Referring the person to another source for an answer.
Lying.

Pretending not to understand the game.

Members of the group concluded that noncommunication is dull, that it is easier to avoid answering than it is to press someone who will not communicate.

SESSION 6—SHOW AND TELL

Prior Preparation Required

At the end of the previous session, participants are asked to bring to today's session some object they have made or produced themselves. It may be an item of handcraft, a hobby exhibit, original writing, or anything else a person wishes to bring. Participants are instructed to bring something they are neither completely proud of nor completely ashamed of.

Organization

Chairs are arranged in a semicircle or concentric semicircles.

Equipment

Dowel sticks about 8 to 12 in. long, 3/8 or 1/2 in. in diameter, one for each participant; self-made items brought by participants.

Instructions

"In turn, each of you will come to the front of the group and talk about the item you have brought. You are to say *what* you like about it and *what* you do not like about it. You are neither to praise your production nor make excuses for what you think is wrong with it. Present yourself to the group without praise, defense, or self-criticism. Do not make any evaluative statements. Tell us why you chose to bring your particular item. Tell us when you made it and how you found the materials. Do not praise or blame yourself or anyone else.

"This is an exercise in presenting yourself without evaluation. The members of the audience will check errors. I will give each member of the group a stick. Any time you hear the person make any type of evaluative remark or place blame on himself or someone else, rap with your stick on the floor, chair, or table. Rap every time this occurs. If your reason for rapping is not apparent to everyone, you may be asked to explain why you rap.

"Is there anyone who does not understand the directions?"

Activity

Members of the group, in turn, present the items they have

NOTE: If this exercise is used, sufficient sessions should be allowed so that each participant has an opportunity to present his own item.

brought to class. After each person has had an opportunity to present his item, the leader conducts a discussion.

Response of the Pilot Group: Instructor's Observations

Members of the group were amused by the sticks and the rapping, but found it difficult to rap. Humor was frequently used to defend an item that was inadequate. No one commented laughingly on the things he did well.

Individual presentations produced lively participation.

Participants found it easier to criticize their own productions than to say something favorable about them.

SESSION 7—RECIPROCITY: ASKING, RECEIVING, AND ACKNOWLEDGING HELP

Organization

Regular classroom seating, with space to walk about between the chairs.

Equipment

Paper and pencil for each participant.

Instructions

"Asking for help is often a difficult thing to do. Today we will practice it. Think of some task or situation with which you would like some help. The help must be something which a person in this class would be able to give. Move around the room and find the person most able to give the kind of help you need. Do not ask for the help. Merely locate the person able to give it.

"Now return to your seats. Write your name in the top right-hand corner of your paper. Next, write the kind of help you would like. Finally, write the name of the person from whom you would like to have this help."

Activity

Members of the class follow the instructions.

Instructions

"Now go to the person whose name you have written down and ask for the help you have designated on your paper."

Activity

Members of the class move around the room asking for help from other participants.

Instructions

"Now, take your seats. Let's talk about your experiences in the process of asking for help."

NOTE: This session confronts the overly dependent person who is reluctant to ask for help and demonstrates the many methods used to avoid asking for help.

Questions for Discussion

1. What was your reason for choosing the person you selected to give you the help?
2. How did the other person respond to your request? Did anyone refuse to give you the help you asked for?
3. Did you acknowledge the response of the other person?
4. Was it really help you asked? If not, what was it?
5. What reasons for asking for help seemed to be legitimate? What reasons seemed not to be legitimate?
6. Why are some people afraid to ask for help?

Response of the Pilot Group

Legitimate Reasons for Asking for Help

Some legitimate reasons for asking for help are to obtain specialized knowledge or know-how; to explore facets or scope of a problem; to share responsibility for the outcome; to save time; to find out what would please someone else.

Reasons for Being Afraid to Ask for Help

Afraid to admit that they need help, individuals avoid asking for it, or ask for it indirectly. "Do you have a key to this door?" instead of "I am locked out. Could you open this door for me?" Sometimes people are afraid to ask for help because they fear they will not want to take the action the other person may suggest.

Afraid of rejection, they avoid it by asking for a commitment before stating what kind of help is needed. "Will you do something for me?" Rejection may also be avoided by seeking help from people in general rather than from one particular individual. "Will someone help me?"

Avoiding asking for help also avoids responsibility, either for one's own actions or for an outcome. An example of this device is asking for a commitment before making one. "What would you like to do on vacation?" A common device is asking someone else to make a choice which is really one's own to make. "Do I need domestic help when I go to work?" Another common device is volunteering the services of another person. "I know Martha would not mind helping you out."

SESSION 8—RECIPROCITY: GIVING AND RECEIVING GIFTS

Rich gifts wax poor when givers prove unkind.
Hamlet, Act III, Scene 1, Line 101

Organization
Regular classroom seating.

Equipment
Slips of construction paper, 2 x 3 in., in three colors, such as yellow, purple, and white; marking pens.

Instructions
"Today we are going to give and receive gifts. You each have a yellow and a purple slip of paper. Write your name on both pieces of paper. Think of a Christmas gift—one costing less than ten dollars—which would do the most for your self-esteem and your sense of well-being. Write this on the yellow slip. On the purple slip of paper, write a Christmas gift—also costing less than ten dollars—which would be most unkind, the one you would least like to receive. Both gifts must be real, tangible, and material, something which could be wrapped. Now take these two slips of paper and put them where no one can see them, in your pocket or purse.

"Next, choose a partner. Within each pair, label one person as No. 1 and the other person as No. 2.

"You will have five minutes for the first part of the exercise. No. 1's, talk to your partners about yourselves. Tell of your likes and dislikes, etc. No. 2's, you are not to give any feedback or respond in any way. Simply listen, and listen as carefully as you can."

Activity
No. 1's talk for five minutes and No. 2's listen.

Instructions
"Now we shall reverse the procedure. No. 2's talk for five

NOTE: As specifically set up, this session applies to Christmas. However, it could be adaptable to gift-giving in general. The exercise points up the hostile feelings which may accompany loving feelings.

minutes. No. 1's listen carefully. Do not give any feedback or respond in any way."

Activity

No. 2's talk for five minutes.

Instructions

"Now separate from your partner and go to a different part of the room. Find a seat. On another yellow slip of paper, write down your partner's name and what you would give your partner if you were going to give him something that would do the most for his self-esteem, his sense of well-being. The present must be a real, material thing, which could be wrapped. It cannot be an intangible concept, such as *happiness*. It must be a real something which could be bought for less than ten dollars.

Activity

Participants follow the directions.

Instructions

"On a purple slip of paper, write the gift you would give your partner if you were going to give him the most unkind gift you could give, one which would express hostility. Again, the gift must be something real, tangible. It cannot be a concept or an idea. It must cost less than ten dollars.

Activity

Participants follow the directions. The instructor passes out the white slips.

Instructions

"On a white slip of paper, write a conditional gift you would give your partner. A conditional gift is one which has strings attached—conditions or limitations on it. This must also be a tangible gift which could be purchased for less than ten dollars. It cannot be an idea or a concept, though it may have ideas or concepts attached to it."

Activity

Participants follow the directions.

Instructions

"Go back to your original seat and your partner. Compare your yellow slip of paper with the one your partner wrote for himself. How similar are the two items? Talk about it."

Activity

Participants follow instructions.

Instructions

"Now compare your purple slips. How much alike are they? Talk about it. What devices did you use to select hostile, unkind gifts?"

Activity

Participants follow instructions and discuss devices used.

Instructions

"Now compare your white slips. What kinds of conditions did you put on the gift? Have you ever received conditional gifts? What feelings does a conditional gift evoke in you? Why?"

Activity

Participants follow instructions.

Questions for Discussion

1. Did you communicate your interests, likes and dislikes well enough for the other person to be able to select a present you liked? That you disliked? What problems did you have in your communication?
2. What devices were used to build self-esteem?
3. What devices were used to express unkindness and hostility through a gift?
4. What ideas have you about conditional gifts? What feelings?

Response of the Pilot Group

Devices for Being Unkind and Hostile Through Gifts

Give a gift I would like, not really being concerned with what the other person would like.

Give a gift, such as dandruff-removing shampoo, which points out something humiliating to the other person.

Give a tool or machine, such as a lawnmower, to accomplish work the person avoids or postpones.

Give something, such as cigarettes, candy or whiskey, to encourage a habit the person is trying to break.

Give a gift, such as a complicated camera, that the person will be unable to use because he can't operate it.

Give a person something which is wholly useless to him.

Theoretical Summary

Although gifts are ostensibly given to express love or esteem, they often carry with them covert hostile messages. The anger thus produced is especially difficult to deal with, since the hostile messages are hidden in an act supposed to evoke appreciation and thanks.

Another method of expressing a hostile message is through a gift with conditions attached. This offering also produces anger; the recipient is trapped because the conditions are covert or are not stated until after the gift has been accepted.

In the giving of a conditional gift, the giver should set forth any limitations before the gift is offered, if he is to avoid hostile expression. This practice allows the recipient to refuse the gift if he does not want to comply with the limitations.

Once the giver proffers the gift, he may entertain hopes or wishes related to the use of the item, but if he is forthright, he does not trap the receiver into compliance. He may express any hopes or wishes he may have, but the other person should feel no obligation to comply with them.

Once the gift has been given, the receiver then owns it and can do with it what he wants. If the receiver is not willing to accept the limitations or conditions set by the giver, he should not accept the gift.

Section V

The Problem-Solving Process

UNIT I—RECOGNIZING AND UNDERSTANDING RESPONSES TO STRESS

SESSION 1—FIGHT AND FLIGHT

It's not the problem which is the problem; it is the solution which is the problem.[1]

Theoretical Presentation

BIOLOGICALLY, EMOTIONS ARE designed to produce fight or flight. In primitive times, fear served a true protective function by injecting hormones into the bloodstream, thus producing a faster heartbeat, adding adrenalin to the blood, and effecting other physiological changes. His fear, therefore, enabled a person to fight danger more fiercely or to flee more rapidly from imminent danger.

Man's emotions still create physiological changes in preparation for fight or flight. Whereas in most cases we can neither fight physically nor literally run from a threatening situation, we devise other methods of response. Unfortunately, many of these responses provide no solution but merely escalate the problem.

When you become frightened or angry, is your basic response one of fight or flight? When presented with a problem, are you inclined to remain and fight in one way or another, or do you flee?

Organization

Regular classroom seating. Participants will subsequently rearrange themselves.

Equipment

Pieces of construction paper, 2 x 3 in., in red and yellow;

NOTE: Polarization of personality types produces catalytic interaction between two divergent groups. The session is not difficult, and group discussion produces interesting conclusions without too much prompting from the instructor.

[1] Gossett, John, Clinical Psychologist, Timberlawn Psychiatric Hospital.

several rolls of transparent tape in dispensers, rubber cement, paper and pencil for each group.

Instructions

"Those of you whose major method of dealing with anger is one of *fight,* select a red tag. Attach it to your shoulder with transparent tape. Those whose major method of dealing with anger is one of *flight,* select a yellow tag. Attach it to your shoulder with transparent tape."

Activity

Participants attach tags to their shoulders. Since some persons will be unable to decide whether their major mechanism is fight or flight, they are given special instructions.

Instructions

"If you are unable to decide which color to wear, try to decide which method you use more often. Take a tag of the color which indicates your major method. Then, tear off a piece of the other color to represent the proportionate extent to which you use the second method. Paste this second piece over the first one."

Activity

The indecisive members create an appropriate combination of colored tags.

Instructions

"Please get together in groups with those who have the same color tag as yours. There will be three groups: the red group, the yellow group, and a group of those with mixed tags.

"In your groups arrange yourselves in a circle so that you can talk to each other. Those in the red group will discuss the methods you use to fight. Those in the yellow group will discuss the methods you use to take flight. The group with two-colored tags will discuss both the methods you use to fight and the methods you use to take flight. In the latter group, try to distinguish between the types of situations which cause you to fight or to take flight.

"Select a secretary or a recorder for your group. The recorder will write the summary of your group discussion."

Activity

The three groups conduct their discussions. The recorder in each group sets down the points which are made.

Instructions

"Now we will hear the report from each recorder, beginning with the red group. The other groups will report in turn."

Activity

The recorder from each group presents his report.

Response of the Pilot Group: Collation

Mechanisms of fight included the following: using profanity, striking someone, throwing things, threatening, using sarcasm or scorn, complaining, harrassing, being irresponsible, acting impulsively.

Mechanisms of flight included leaving the scene, rationalizing, withdrawing, changing the subject, being silent, pouting, not listening, using drugs and alcohol, sleeping, procrastinating, daydreaming, crying, fantasizing, misdirecting anger to someone else.

Mechanisms of mixed fight and flight included the following: apologizing, pitying oneself, bringing in a third party, treading lightly on others' feelings, acting weak to avoid attack.

SESSION 2—PERCENTAGES OF CONTROL

Organization

Regular classroom seating.

Equipment

Paper and pencil for each participant.

Instructions

"Write your name in the top right-hand corner of the paper.

"What part do you have in determining your future? Presume that your situation is exactly as it is at this moment. All the features of your life are exactly as they are now. One hundred percent represents total control of your own future and zero percent represents total control by others or by circumstances. Write the percentage of your control. Write a percentage between one hundred and zero at the top of the paper under your name."

Activity

Each participant determines a percentage and writes it at the top of his paper.

Instructions

"Next, number down the left-hand column from one to five. Itemize five ways in which you could increase your ability to determine your future."

Activity

Each participant lists five ways he could increase participation in controlling his future. Those who have stated their future is one hundred percent within their control will point out that nothing can be done to increase their participation. The instructor casually accepts this fact and collects their papers. They are then excused from the room and asked to return ten minutes before the end of the period.

When those remaining have finished, they are divided into three groups (more if needed) according to the percentages they have written on their papers. Those with the highest percentages are put into one group, those with the lowest in another group, and those with median percentages in a third group. A discussion is conducted concerning degrees of control and the allowances which must be made for contingencies.

Questions for Discussion

1. Why did you select the percentage you designated?
2. How do you feel about those with a higher percentage than yours?
3. How do you feel about those with a lower percentage than yours?
4. How do you feel about those who answered one hundred percent?

Response of the Pilot Group: Instructor's Observations

The participants remaining in the room stated that they thought the one hundred percent people did not want to relate to others and feared that the participation of others would disturb their sense of control. A member of the group pointed out that a one hundred percent answer might indicate that a person was afraid that others might change him in a way he did not want to be changed. Another said that our culture endorses such platitudes as "I am the master of my fate" and "He can do anything who dares," etc. However, participants were unable to express their ideas directly to the one hundred percent group when the latter returned to the classroom.

Eight participants out of forty-one answered one hundred percent. Other answers ranged from ninety to twenty percent.

SESSION 3—SELF-CONTRIBUTED CONTINGENCY: LUCK

Theoretical Presentation

We are all aware that there are certain situations over which we undoubtedly have no control. For instance, while traveling on a plane that crashes after being hit by lightning, passengers have no control over the situation. The deaths of these persons could not conceivably be labelled as suicide. Such a calamity is labeled *contingency,* that is, something completely beyond control. We are all subject to contingency.

Man's persistent superstition and his use of the talisman suggest his omnipotent wish to control *fate*—not only his own—but *fate* in general. At the same time, his magical beliefs hint delicately and tactfully at what we all know to be fact—that our own behavior to some extent influences the happenings which occur and the vagaries of fate that pursue us. When we say that someone is *spoiling for trouble,* we are suggesting that his own behavior will produce trouble for him.

We have all known people who are *accident prone.* Statistics reveal that a small percentage of automobile drivers are responsible for a large percentage of the accidents. Carelessness reputedly causes most home accidents. Casually tossed matches ignite most forest fires. Poor health habits account for many illnesses.

Although each of us is subject to various contingencies in life, we are not flotsam and jetsam, idly tossed by the capricious winds of contingency. Each of us, at least to some extent, contributes to consequence. We compound the effects of contingency when we add self-contributed elements to ordinary human error and actual contingency.

Let us begin, for example, with a traffic violation of which all of us are probably guilty on occasion—namely, running a red light. This human error can and often does result from inattentiveness and preoccupation. Let us suppose I commit such a violation.

NOTE: This session is a lecture, followed by a discussion in which individual participants suggest ideas which the instructor writes on the chalkboard.

If a policeman is present at the intersection where I run the red light, the result for me will be a traffic citation and a fine. If I am "lucky," no car was coming and I avoided causing an accident.

Let us see what will happen if I compound the situation with other actions clearly within my control.

I run a red light while speeding.

I run a red light while speeding in a school zone.

I run a red light while speeding in a school zone and while I am driving without a license.

I run a red light while speeding in a school zone and while I am driving without a license and am intoxicated.

I run a red light while speeding in a school zone and while I am driving without a license and am intoxicated and driving a stolen car.

When I compound my initial transgression by adding other self-contributed factors within my control, I rapidly escalate the extent and seriousness of the consequences. I add a number of traffic violations, each of which carries its own penalty. I progress from minor misdemeanors to major misdemeanors and finally felonies, which may result in lengthy confinement in the penitentiary. If I repeat any of the actions, I further escalate the consequences, since the law has provisions for the enhancement of penalties for subsequent convictions.

Organization

Regular classroom seating. Participants will subsequently divide into small discussion groups.

Equipment

Chalkboard and chalk.

Instructions

"Let us now list factors within the driver's control—factors which would increase the destructiveness of driving a car."

Response of the Pilot Group: Summary of Discussion

Some factors which would increase the destructiveness of driving a car are

Driving in bad weather.
Car in poor mechanical condition.
Bad brakes.
Worn tires.
Excessive speed.
Flirting while driving.
Dragging.
Inexperience in driving.
Not wearing safety belts.
Driving too slowly.
Drinking while driving.
Driving barefoot.
Driving bumper to bumper.
Overcrowding of passengers.
Driving while emotionally upset—using the car as a hostile
     weapon.
Driving while physically ill or otherwise incapacitated.

Instructions

"Meet in small groups of eight to ten people and discuss the ways in which you contribute to your own pain. Form the groups in any way you wish."

Activity

Participants meet in groups and discuss self-contributed contingency. At the end of the period, a summary is made and salient comments are written on the chalkboard.

Instructor's Summary

Maxim

You may eventually be crucified
But you don't have to sharpen the axe
Go out and cut down the tree
Buy the nails
And build your own cross.

SESSION 4—IMPULSIVENESS AND PAIN

Theoretical Presentation

Failure to control impulsive behavior usually results in pain for the individual. When a person behaves in a manner which is contrary to the mores of the society in which he lives, he suffers punishment from his society. When he behaves in a manner which is contrary to his own standards, he suffers guilt and remorse. Either type of consequence is painful physically, economically, socially, or psychologically. All of us are impulsive in certain ways and controlled in other ways—impulsive at some times and controlled at other times. Today we will examine degrees of impulsiveness and occasions when this impulsiveness entails more than its worth in resultant pain.

Organization

Regular classroom seating.

Equipment

Tags of brown and orange construction paper, 4 x 4 in.; rubber cement, scissors, transparent tape, marking pens for each participant.

Instructions

"All of us can rate ourselves somewhere on a scale between the two extremes of total control and total impulsiveness.

"Take one orange tag and one brown tag. The orange tags represent impulsiveness and the brown tags represent control. Use for a background the color you think most representative of your overall behavior. On top of the background color, paste a piece of the other color in a size indicating the proportions of impulsiveness and control in you. Write your name on your tag."

Activity

Each member of the group makes himself a tag graphically representing the extent of his impulsiveness and his control.

Instructions

"Each of you should now find someone whose tag is similar

to yours. Discuss with him the types of pain which result from your impulsiveness."

Activity

Participants pair with those having similar tags and discuss the pain which results from impulsiveness. When the discussion has subsided, the instructor asks participants for the major points discovered. These are written on the chalkboard in a summary of the lesson.

The brown and orange tags are collected for use in the following period.

Response of the Pilot Group

Quotations

"Impulsiveness provides a temporary tranquilizer to deal with anxiety. Even knowledge of the consequences is overridden by the need to deal with the anxiety."

"A desperate need for acceptance drives me to a gambling casino where people will call me by name and indicate their acceptance. It is often painful in terms of the cost."

"In rebellion against being controlled, I often become impulsive in an effort to regain control of the situation. I lose control in order to regain control."

"In considering impulsiveness, I not only have to deal with painful consequences from society but with painful consequences within my own conscience."

Summary Collation

Some consequent pain is psychic pain: guilt, depression, fear, anger, loneliness, indecision. Other consequent pain from impulsiveness results from a violation of nature's or society's laws: death, injury, obesity, drunkenness, abandonment, ostracism, termination of employment, criminal conviction.

SESSION 5—LEARNING CONTROL: T MINUS THIRTY AND HOLDING

Theoretical Presentation

In this lesson, the launching of a space rocket will be used to exemplify impulsiveness. The firing and explosive launching have a totality of irrevocability which is indeed like impulsive action—once taken, it can never be retracted.

As you know, in the launching of a space rocket there is a countdown, which is begun at a given time before blast-off, with the time in minutes and seconds counted backwards. T stands for time of blast-off. T minus thirty means thirty minutes before blast-off. The countdown provides time for numerous checks to determine whether all systems are go. The countdown halts immediately if there appears any indication of trouble. This halt is called holding, and countdown proceeds only when the trouble has been corrected. Once the explosive firing sequence has begun, the process is irreversible.

Today we are going to practice postponing impulsive action for thirty minutes. For this reason, the lesson is called "T Minus Thirty and Holding."

Organization

Regular classroom seating.

Equipment

Pieces of clothesline 3 ft. long or strips of cloth 2 in. wide and 3 ft. long, one piece for each two participants; brown and orange tags from the previous session.

Instructions

"Put on your tags saved from the previous session. Those of you who had brown tags or principally brown tags select and stand beside a partner who had an orange tag or a tag that was primarily orange. Now, tie your inside ankles together with this piece of rope. You will then be hobbled. Do you know what

------

NOTE: In this session, the capabilities and knowledge of one personality type are used to teach those of another personality type. The exercise is supportive for those teaching and provocative for those learning.

a hobble actually is and what it is used for? It is a strap or rope used to tie together the legs of a horse or mule so that he cannot run away. The orange tags are now hobbled so that they cannot run away.

"The impulsive people are inhibited by the controlled people, who will serve as teachers today. Your job is to help teach the impulsive people how to control their impulses.

"With your partner, you will go for a walk. Go wherever you want to go on the grounds. During the walk, the impulsive orange-tag person will probably get an urge to do something. As you get the urge, you are to talk to your brown-tag control about the urge you have. Stop walking and start talking the minute you have an urge to do something impulsive. Talk until you have examined all of the possible complications you can think of. You are holding. Do not do anything. Do not take any impulsive action you may have in mind. When you cannot think of any more consequences to talk about, you may resume your walk. If an impulsive action occurs to you again, stop and talk about it until you have exhausted the potential troubles which might arise if you proceeded with your impulsive action. You will spend thirty minutes on this exercise. For thirty minutes, no matter what urges you to blast off, you will hold while you check out possible troublesome situations.

"Remember, we call this lesson "T Minus Thirty and Holding." Regardless of what impulsive act you conceive, you will do nothing about it for thirty minutes. At the end of thirty minutes, you will resume class and talk about your experience.

"Those of you with brown tags are the hobble. Your task is to keep your impulsive partner from taking any impulsive action. You will assist him in examining the trouble spots in his situation and keep him from running away."

Activity

Partners, hobbled together, go for their 30-minute walk. At the end of the allotted time, the instructor rings a bell or gives some other signal to notify participants to return to the classroom for a discussion of their experiences. When all have returned, the instructor collects the tags and keeps them for use in succeeding periods.

Questions for Discussion

1. Orange tags, how did you feel during the exercise?
2. Brown tags, how did you feel during the exercise?
3. When are the consequences of impulsiveness the most painful?
4. How can impulsiveness be modified to make the consequences less painful?

Response of the Pilot Group: Quotations from Participants

"I gave in to my impulses before the end of thirty minutes and doubled the problem."

"I held out for thirty minutes but did something else to create the same problem."

"I had the impulse to express anger. I waited for thirty minutes and then bawled out someone else for not expressing *my* thoughts."

"I had the impulse to make a request and then changed my mind about what I wanted."

"I said some words but did not express anything."

"I wanted to express anger. I waited thirty minutes, then giggled."

"I gave up, deciding that others would have reacted if I had said anything."

"I had the impulse to hug someone and didn't get to do it."

The consequences of impulsiveness are most painful . . .

"When the act is irrevocable."

"When the action repeats itself and you feel helpless to avoid the repetition."

"When the act results in being separated from people you don't want to be separated from."

"When someone else's life depends on your having control and you lose control (hit-and-run accident)."

"When you run from situations which offer hope for help with desperate problems."

"When you run away at a time when you are desperately needed by others."

Impulsiveness can be modified to make the consequences less
painful . . .

"By postponing the action longer than you have in the past."

"By reducing the volume of the action."

"By reducing the intensity of the action."

"By reducing the frequency of the action."

"By taking the action within the bounds of more acceptable
behavior."

"By anticipating the results of the action and planning
accordingly."

"By changing the situation or context of the action."

"By informing the person you are acting against so that he can
anticipate it."

SESSION 6—LEARNING TO BE IMPULSIVE

Theoretical Presentation

Some people are too impulsive. Others are too inhibited. The behavior of the overcontrolled person is characterized by conscientiousness, marked inhibition, and inflexible adherence to rigid standards. To obtain this degree of control, such people argue with themselves, rationalize, excuse others, and employ all sorts of erasing and delaying tactics to keep themselves from taking action. Their behavior is so controlled that occasionally they are compelled to explode and act violently. Such people need to learn to be more spontaneous, more impulsive in small ways about small things more frequently. In this way, they avoid the build-up of tension.

Today we are going to try to teach these overly rigid people to do something spontaneous—to be more impulsive than they are.

Organization

Regular classroom seating.

Equipment

Brown and orange tags from the previous period, dowel sticks, transparent tape.

Instructions

"Attach your own tag to your shoulder with transparent tape. Each brown tag should select an orange tag for a partner. You may have the same partner you had in the hobble lesson or you may choose a different partner.

"Today the orange tags will serve as teachers. You will go in pairs for a 30-minute walk, as you did in the previous lesson. If the brown tag person gets an inclination to do something impulsive, the orange tag person will prod him to do it and to do it right away.

"To prod means literally to poke or to jab with something pointed. The figurative meaning is to seek to rouse or incite to

NOTE: This session produces anger in overcontrolled persons, especially if the physical prod is used.

action. Orange tags are first to use verbal prods. If this is unproductive, the orange tag may use the dowel stick to help the brown-tag person do something which is impulsive.

"There are three rules: (a) You cannot destroy property; (b) you cannot be physically destructive to others; (c) you cannot be destructive to yourself.

"At the end of thirty minutes, you will return to the classroom to talk about your experiences."

Activity

Partners leave the classroom for their 30-minute walk. At the end of the time, the instructor rings a bell or gives some other signal. Participants return to the classroom for a discussion of their experiences.

The instructor collects the brown and orange tags for use in succeeding periods.

SESSION 7—IMPULSIVENESS AND ANGER

Organization

Regular classroom seating.

Equipment

The brown and orange tags from the previous periods, sheets of red construction paper, scissors, transparent tape, rubber cement.

Instructions

"You have previously made brown and orange tags for yourselves, the brown tags representing the extent to which you are controlled and the orange tags the extent to which you are impulsive. Brown and orange combinations were to represent the proportions of your behavior which are controlled or impulsive.

"It was suggested that impulsive behavior occurs as an effort to relieve anxiety, to serve as a kind of tranquilizer when tension becomes too great to be tolerable.

"Let us now consider to what extent impulsiveness is the result of anger. How much of your impulsiveness is an expression of anger? How much of your control is control of anger? We have here some red paper which will stand for anger. Do you think that red underlies the orange and brown on your tag? If you believe that anger produces in you the need for either impulsiveness or for control, substitute red paper for a portion of the brown or orange paper."

Activity

Members of the group decide whether or not to substitute red paper for a portion of their brown and orange tags.

Instructions

"Those of you who have put some red on your tags to indicate that anger is involved in your impulsiveness or your control,

---

NOTE: This discussion session is designed to point up the anger component in impulsive action. Those who demonstrate insight teach those who are unable to understand the relationship between anger and hasty action.

please pair off with someone who has no red on his tag. Those with the red on their tags are to serve as teachers. Those who still have only orange and brown tags will be the students. One teacher may have several students, or one student may have several teachers. You must be either teacher or pupil."

Activity

The instructor assists with the grouping.

Instructions

"Teachers, see if you can help the student ferret out some element of anger in situations in which he is impulsive or over-controlled. Try to help him discover the source of his anger."

Activity

Teachers and students discuss impulsiveness and control.

At the end of the period, participants return to their seats, and the instructor conducts a discussion about the types of experiences they have had and the insights they have achieved. Salient points are written on the chalkboard. The exercise concludes with a theoretical summary.

Theoretical Summary

Instead of solving problems, expression through impulsive action escalates problems. If consequent pain is to be avoided, verbal expressiveness must substitute for impulsive action. If we are to be mentally healthy, our goal is to remove all self-contributed contingency from our behavior in order to avoid any pain not justified by the accomplishment.

Lack of verbal expressiveness is equally hazardous for the impulsive person and the overcontrolled person. When the impulsive person becomes anxious, he does not express his anxiety verbally but acts impulsively. The impulsive actions produce painful consequences which further escalate his anxiety. The escalated anxiety demands more impulsive action, thus entangling the person in a self-contributed spiral of misfortune.

When the controlled person becomes anxious, he expresses nothing verbally but institutes further and more stringent controls on himself in order to allay his anxiety. His stringent controls produce additional anxiety that in turn calls for still-stronger controls. Finally, in order to break out of his self-created prison, the overcontrolled person engages in impulsive action. This impulsive action creates pain which increases his anxiety, and again he faces the need for more controls.

In either case, we have a vicious circle. The only escape is through verbal expressiveness, which obviates the need for either impulsive behavior or further stringent controls. The goal is to substitute verbal expressiveness for impulsive action *and* for excessive control.

UNIT II—CONSTRUCTIVE SELF-ASSERTION

SESSION 1—THE NEED FOR SELF-ASSERTION: ATTACK, DEFENSE, TRESPASS, REBUFF AND COUNTERATTACK

Theoretical Presentation

IN THE COURSE OF group living, in which all of us participate every day of our lives, we are involved, of necessity, in many encounters. Some encounters we initiate; some are initiated by others. Some approaches are hostile, some friendly. Some of our activities are clearly defensive, while others are clearly predatory. Some activities fall between attack and defense.

In order to be sensitively aware of the differences among territory of the self, the common ground, and the spaces of others, one must first have a clearly defined concept of one's boundaries. In previous lessons we have made efforts to define boundaries and become more aware of our delimitations.

Each of us has a life space within which we have a right and an obligation to live. Our right is related to possession and manifestation of our inner self. Defense of boundaries may become necessary to maintain the continuance of our selfhood. Our need now is to define these boundaries more specifically and to study examples of defense, negotiation, and attack.

Such definition is closely related to problems of anger, to self-expression, and in the final analysis, to mental health, self-actualization, or authenticity, since the latter are functions of the process of learning to live comfortably within the space we have, of filling it completely, and consequently experiencing fulfillment. First, let us examine the terminology.

Attack implies initiative. An attack is the initial movement in a performance. Attack signals the beginning of hostilities and

---

NOTE: This session is complex and difficult, requiring discriminatory ability on the part of the instructor and the participants. The exercise is unsuitable for the naive or the participant of limited intelligence.

is ever more potent if deliberately and definitely planned. An attack is not necessarily physical but may include unfavorable criticism, argument, censure, blame, or verbal abuse.

Defense, the opposite of attack, implies that some other person or force has taken the initiative in the situation, and one's defense is a resistance to, or protection against, attack.

Counterattack is a form of defense but suggests a greater degree of activity than the more passive defense. Violence may be actual or implied.

A rebuff is a refusal to accept the encounter itself. It is a sharp check and indicates that no further negotiations are desired.

To trespass is to make an improper inroad on a person's presence, time or interests. A trespass is a crowding of the rights of another person, an overstepping of his rightful boundaries by a wrongful entry. Trespass includes intrusion and encroachment.

An intrusion is a kind of trespass in that a person thrusts himself into the presence of another person or into places or circumstances where he is not welcome.

An encroachment is a gradual and stealthy inroad upon the territory, rights and privileges of another, so that a foothold is imperceptibly established. Thus an encroachment is also a form of trespass.

Each adult is expected to take the responsibility for his own defense. Whereas children may need to be protected from others, adulthood implies the ability for self-defense. If others attack our territory or trespass upon it, it is our responsibility to defend it.

Further, we are expected to negotiate the joint use of the common ground which we hold congruently with others. Cooperative tasks and cooperative use imply cooperative decisions.

Finally, we must necessarily refrain from predatory or exploitative forays into the life space of others and withdraw willingly from their space when we find that we are trespassing upon their areas. If we fail to withdraw voluntarily from the territorial claims of others, society grants the other individual the right of forcible ejection or recourse to delegated authorities whose duty it is to forcibly eject us and punish us for our trespassing.

In the discussion of common, everyday occurrences, let us try to identify attacks, defenses, counterattacks, rebuffs, and trespasses. Later we will examine the kinds of interactions which promote relatedness.

Organization

Participants are seated in groups around tables.

Equipment

Paper and pencil for each participant, red marking pens for each group.

Instructions

"Divide your paper into two columns. Write your name in the top right-hand corner of your paper.

"In the left-hand column, write something annoying which someone said to you. In the right-hand column, put your response. Continue to itemize segments of interchanges. We will spend about fifteen minutes writing."

Activity

Participants record interchanges they have had with others.

Instructions

"In your groups, each of you will read an interchange you have written. Discuss it in your group and decide whether the person is making an attack, a defense, a counterattack, a rebuff, or a trespass statement. Write your classifications with the red pen. Continue with this procedure until you have decided upon the nature of each statement and each response."

Activity

Participants follow the instructions.

Instructions

"Let's hear the report from each group. Did you have difficulties in making the classifications? Read us statements which are the clearest and best examples, and tell us how you have classified them. Explain your thinking process or the reasons you have used for making your decisions."

Activity

Each group in turn gives a report as instructed. (The classification and reporting may require more than one period.)

Response of the Pilot Group: Quotations from Participants

Attacks

"I'll just have to decide. You are too immature and irresponsible to make a decision."

"You just don't know how to handle money."

"You are too particular."

"If you don't stop acting so righteous, I won't be your friend any more."

"If you don't give me a visit this weekend, I'm leaving the hospital."

Trespasses

"I told Mary you were in a psychiatric hospital. There is no reason you should mind."

"I got your emery board out of your drawer."

"I played your records. Anyway, they're already scratched."

"I threw your white shoes away. You don't wear them anyway."

"I showed your poems to my friends. They liked some of them."

"You shouldn't feel that way about anyone."

"I don't know whether to tell you this because I know what your reaction will be."

"I let Joe borrow your car. I figured you could ride with someone else."

"What did you and your doctor talk about today?"

"I'm only trying to do what is best for you."

Rebuffs

"I am going to do what I want to, and I don't care whether you like it or not."

"That's just the way I am."

"I don't want to discuss the subject any more. Let's drop it."

"I want to go to the store. Since you don't, you can sit at home. I'll have the car."

"So what! I've been hurt by people before. You don't bother me."

"I feel depressed. Just leave me alone."

"I can do it myself. I *can* do a *few* things on my own, you know!"

"I'm not going on making small talk any longer, and if you don't like it you can lump it."

"If you don't want to do what I want to do, you can just flake off. I'll do it by myself."

"Since you don't want to be with me, I certainly can get along without you."

"O.K. Go on and do it by yourself, but don't call on me when you need help."

Counterattacks

"You just don't know all I've been through."

"You think you are perfect."

"You are in for a rude awakening."

"You are too sensitive."

"I don't see how you can call me immature when you have a lot of growing up to do yourself."

"It is inexcusable to think that."

"You are not nice when you're mad."

Appropriate Defenses

"I'm sorry you don't enjoy talking this early in the morning. I enjoy chatting at breakfast."

"I realize how you feel, but I need to make my own decisions."

"I felt tired, so I didn't finish everything. I get frustrated when I get behind in my work."

"I feel bad and don't want to talk right now."

"I have to cry a little to get the anger and guilt feelings out."

"I have told you the way I feel. Each person is entitled to his feelings."

SESSION 2—ADEQUATE DEFENSE: STANDING IN YOUR OWN FOOTPRINTS

Organization

Regular classroom seating, provided there is a space at the front in which the exercise can be conducted. If not, chairs will have to be moved to make a suitable space.

Equipment

Two sets of footprints, life-size, cut out of colored cardboard; masking tape to attach the footprints to the floor. The left and right footprints should be a little apart from each other (4-12 in.) and the pairs of footprints should be placed facing each other, yet far enough apart that the participants cannot reach or touch each other (8-12 ft. apart).

Instructions

"We need two volunteers to participate in this exercise. We will need two more later and possibly several more sets of two during the period."

Activity

Two volunteers come forward.

Instructions

"Each of you stand in a set of footprints, facing each other. You are to engage in a verbal battle. No matter what happens, you are not to move your feet out of your own footprints. Each of you will try to get the other person to abandon his footprints. You may say anything you think would help you in your attempt to get the other person to abandon his footprints.

"Are there any questions? If not, go ahead with the battle."

Activity

The two volunteers proceed with the verbal battle in an attempt to get the other person to move out of his own footprints.

If neither person moves, the battle is considered a draw after five minutes. When one person moves, the exercise concludes with a discussion of the devices used in attack and those used in defense. When the discussion subsides, other volunteers repeat the procedure. Near the end of the period the instructor conducts a summarizing discussion.

Theoretical Summary

The footprints symbolize your self, your rights, your personality, your identity. In order to conduct an adequate defense, it is necessary to learn to engage in interpersonal conflict without abandoning the self by attacking the other person or by abnegating one's own rights or responsibilities. Defense without attack, rebuff, or counterattack is difficult.

SESSION 3—LINE-UP AT THE TRADING STAMP STORE

Theoretical Presentation

While travelling in England several years ago, I was impressed with the severe scorn the British level at those who fail to line up properly. Their term is *queueing up*.

Once, in a bank, there were two lines of customers *queued up*. I approached the wicket merely to ask whether I was in the proper line; I had no intention of breaking in. But the British citizenry waiting in line were so suspect and scornful of my manners that I whimpered an apology and returned to my original place in line without the necessary information.

Americans are filled with contradictions regarding the execution of their rights. We exalt *fair play*, yet in many situations unfair play is acceptably cloaked with the concept, "If you don't look out for yourself, nobody else will." People laughingly advise, "Do unto others before they have time to do unto you." "Be aggressive." "If you want it, get it." "If you are not a go-getter, you will get nowhere." "Push." "Get ahead." "Get in front of everybody else if you can."

Since such aggressiveness overrides politeness, we need to learn constructive self-defense and constructive self-assertion for survival in the American culture.

Let us see how well we do with this concept in an experimental situation.

Organization

Chairs are pushed back against the wall, with a space cleared in the center of the classroom. A table is placed at one side of this cleared space.

Equipment

Consecutively numbered paper tickets. There should be one less ticket than the number of people in the class.

NOTE: This session is again aimed at those who try to avoid conflict. The success of the confrontation depends upon selection of those who are to play the various roles. Very aggressive, manipulative persons must be those chosen to break into the line. The storekeeper should be a compulsive, dutiful person who will not lose his role or participate in the conflicts among those in the line-up.

Instructions

"We need some special volunteers for today's experiment. These should be people who experience little difficulty in being aggressive when the situation demands it. Which of you can fill this role?"

Activity

When four people have volunteered, the instructor takes them aside and tells them that their role will be to try to cheat in line, to get ahead of their allotted place to one which is nearer the front of the line. They are instructed to use any ruse to accomplish their purpose. The four people return to the class after they have received their instructions.

Instructions

"We need one person to be the store clerk. Who likes keeping store and will take the role of storekeeper?" (A volunteer is selected.)

"Today we are going to enact a scene at a trading stamp store. I will give each of you a number so that you will know your proper place in this line. You will turn in imaginary books of trading stamps. The storekeeper will take your stamps and in return give you imaginary merchandise of your selection."

Activity

The storekeeper takes a place behind the table. The numbers are passed out and the participants line up in front of the table according to their numbers. The instructor passes out the slips so that the four who have instructions to cheat in line receive numbers that are separated and not too close to the head of the line. (i.e., 4, 9, 13, 18.) The exact position is not important.

As each person is waited on, the next in line offers his imaginary books of trading stamps, and the storekeeper produces imaginary merchandise. Interaction follows between those in their correct places in line and those who attempt to cheat to get a more favorable position.

The activity is continued until the time has run out or until the interest subsides. Participants return to their seats for discussion of their experiences.

Questions for Discussion

1. How did you respond when someone tried to get in front of you?
2. What methods did people use to manipulate a better position in line?
3. What methods have you observed others using in a similar situation?
4. Did you respond as you usually do when someone tries to get ahead of you?
5. Do you ever try to get ahead of others in line?
6. Which types of self-defense and self-assertion do you consider constructive?

Response of the Pilot Group: Quotations from Participants

"When they got ahead, it was not a problem to me."

"Other people seemed to be more in a hurry, so I didn't mind if they got ahead."

"It was more aggravating to hold your own than to let them in."

"The problem was not important enough to do anything about it. I will do something about more important things."

"I figured someone else would take care of it."

"I wasn't the only one it happened to."

"I knew it wouldn't do any good to say anything."

"Whoever was in charge should have made provisions that were fair."

SESSION 4—DON'T THROW THE BABY OUT
WITH THE BATHWATER

Theoretical Presentation

A concern for communication presupposes that the individual is concerned about the relationship involved and wants to further and develop this relationship. Otherwise, relationships one does not wish to keep may be broken off. If it is desired to keep a relationship, both positive and negative expressions must be included. Expressions which threaten the very existence of the relationship should be avoided, as they do nothing to further relatedness.

Concern for the persistence of a relationship is implicit in positive expressions; consequently these positive expressions are not relatedness-threatening. The problem arises most specifically in relation to expressions of angry, hostile, negative feelings. When expressing such feelings, one must keep it clear that the expression in no way threatens the existence of the relationship itself. Angry, hostile expressions should clarify the causes of the anger and vivify the feelings involved without including suggestions or implications that the relationship itself is not desired or desirable.

An old proverb says, "Don't throw the baby out with the bathwater." In other words, in order to get rid of something we don't want, we should not throw out what we do want. We don't have to throw out the good simply to get rid of the bad.

Today we will demonstrate ways in which we express anger in relationship-breaking statements.

Organization

Regular classroom seating, with a space at the front of the room where two chairs, six to ten feet apart, face each other.

Equipment

A dowel stick, 3/8 x 12 in., for each participant.

Instructions

"To start today's lesson, we need a volunteer. (Someone raises his hand.) Please come to the front and sit in one of these chairs. Now select someone in the class with whom you would like to pick a fight. He will sit in the other chair. (The person selected comes forward.)

"The two of you are going to start a fight with each other. Each of you will try to express your feelings on some subject.

"Those of you in the audience will listen carefully to what is said. Any time one of these two people makes a statement which *throws out the baby with the bathwater*—that is, threatens to break off the relationship—please rap with your sticks.

"You two at the front are to stop when you hear the rap of a stick. At that point we will try to analyze what the person has said that is actually *throwing out the baby with the bathwater*. First, the person who rapped will attempt to explain why he has rapped. Others in the group may be able to help or add to his explanation.

"Are the instructions clear? Do you know when you are to rap with your sticks? Let me state it again. Whenever one of these two people says something which threatens to break off the relationship, you will rap.

"Suppose in the course of the interchange, one person says, 'Why don't you go fly a kite?' He has suggested that he would be better off if the other person were not present, were far away, did not exist. This statement *throws the baby out with the bathwater*. Let's try it and see how it goes."

Activity

The two volunteers at the front engage in a verbal fight. Members of the group rap with their sticks whenever a statement threatens to break off the relationship. When anyone raps, he is asked to explain what has been said or done to cause him to rap with his stick.

As each statement is identified as threatening to the relationship, the instructor writes it on the chalkboard. At the end of the period, a summary is made of statements which endanger a relationship.

Response of the Pilot Group: Summary of Discussion

The pilot group developed the following suggestions to avoid throwing the baby out with the bathwater:

Do not defend your action—just your right to choose the action.

Don't bolster yourself with someone else's opinion.

Don't defend by counterattack.

Don't defend by telling the other person he has no right to do or say what he is doing or saying.

SESSION 5—CHARACTERISTICS OF RELATIONSHIP INTERCHANGES

Theoretical Presentation

In the foregoing lessons, we have talked extensively about the feelings which lie inside each of us and of the various ways to manifest these feelings.

There is still another kind of communication which arises directly from an awareness of others and verbal acknowledgment of such awareness. This kind of communication we shall call *relationship interchanges*. These expressions emphasize the interactional process itself. In such exchanges, the messages "I am concerned about you," and "Are you concerned about me?" are altered to the acknowledgment, "We are concerned about each other." Each person thereby acknowledges the participation of the other in the situation and gives his response to this participation. Relationship interchanges are not expressions of *personal* feelings but are expressions of *interpersonal* feelings.

Today we will examine the kinds of communication which express relatedness and those which express nonrelatedness.

Organization

Usual classroom seating.

Equipment

Green construction paper tags, 2 x 3 in.; transparent tape.

Instructions

"I will give each of you a number of green tickets.

"In this exercise you will try to express relatedness. You will wander about the room, go up to someone, and make some kind of relatedness statement. If you do this successfully, the person you are talking to will give you a green ticket. If any person makes a relatedness statement to you, try to respond with another relatedness statement. If this person thinks you have done it successfully, he will give you a green ticket.

"You cannot give tickets to yourself. Another person must give you a ticket.

"Keep separate the tickets you earn and those you have to

give to others. Put the tickets you earn in your pocket or purse. Keep in your hand the tickets you give out. The object is to earn as many green tickets as possible. Try to stay aware of the nature of relationship interchanges.

"After you have had a series of interchanges with one person and have earned or failed to earn tickets, you should move on, going from person to person as long as we continue this part of the exercise.

"Remember, you cannot give tickets to yourself."

Activity

After the instructor distributes the tickets, the participants move about the room in conversation. Fifteen or twenty minutes before the end of the period, the instructor stops the activity and recognizes those who have earned the largest number of tickets. There follows a summary discussion on the nature of relationship interchanges.

Questions for Discussion
1. How do people behave when they express relatedness?
2. How do people behave when they express unrelatedness?
3. How do you feel when you feel related?
4. How do you feel when you feel unrelated?
5. In your interchanges, did you discover some good examples of relationship interchanges? What were they? Can you add examples from other situations?

Response of the Pilot Group: Quotations from Participants
When people express relatedness . . .
"They pay attention to you."
"They respond warmly."
"They provide moral support."
"They provide company, companionship."
"They share themselves."
When people express unrelatedness . . .
"They ignore you, are indifferent."
"They are cold and hostile."
"They don't care, they are self-centered."
"They say 'That's your problem.'"

"They are withdrawn and alienated."

"They bottle up, hold back, relate only superficially."

"Things are inconclusive, unresolved."

When you feel related . . .

"You understand them and they understand you."

"You feel with them and for them."

"You feel close to them."

"You feel comfortable, casual."

"You have a sense of physical contact and awareness."

"You share your belongings."

"You give each other help."

When you feel unrelated . . .

"Both of you are unfeeling."

"There is no feeling. You push them away."

"You are restless, uneasy, forced, selfish."

"You feel revulsion, avoidance, attack."

"You are stingy, blind to the other's need."

"You hinder each other, ignore needs, and refuse to help."

SESSION 6—HOW TO EXPRESS FEELINGS
WITHOUT HURTING PEOPLE

Theoretical Presentation

One of the major concerns stated by those who have difficulty expressing feelings is that they will hurt someone's feelings if they say what they would really like to say. In most cases, however, hurt has to do with the way in which we express feelings, not with what is expressed. In most cases, the other person is already aware that some kind of difficulty is involved in a certain topic or situation.

It is far more likely that we are afraid to express feelings because we fear retaliation—that the other person will respond by hurting us. Because of our fear, because adequate expression of feelings is difficult, and because of inexperience, we are likely to perform poorly in expressing ourselves. The unfortunate results of each bungled attempt increase our anxiety.

In this session, certain principles are suggested as possibly helpful. We will practice some interchanges, attempting to put these principles into action:

1. *Examine your own feelings.* If you are overly concerned about hurting someone if you express your feelings, it is probably because the feelings you have to express would really hurt, and basically you would like to hurt the other person. If this is the case, it will be virtually impossible for you to express yourself without causing hurt, even though you try to hide your feelings. In such an instance, it is probably better to say nothing and spend further time trying to understand yourself—or if you know the person well, risk saying "I feel like hurting you because. . . ."

2. *Acknowledge that when two people are involved, there are bound to be differences.* People have different values and different needs. It is necessary that you express *your* point of view, and try to understand the problem from the point of view of the other person. If you both held the same priorities of importance, he probably would not be doing what is creating the

---

NOTE: In this session practical suggestions are offered on expressiveness and means of accomplishing it. These suggestions are then put into practice.

problem for you. Explain not only that the problem is important to you, but tell the other person why. Ask him whether he feels the same way, or ask him to explain how he feels differently. Say, "From my point of view. . . ."

3. *Acknowledge aloud the good will of the other person.* Acknowledge verbally that the other person is probably as anxious to find a solution to the problem as you are. Presume that the person would not have knowingly done what has annoyed or upset you, and voice your presumption that he will be glad to have something worked out.

4. *Consider the problem as a separate entity.* No one person constitutes a problem; both of you are involved in it. Include yourself as part of the problem. "Let's look at the problem and see if we can come up with something." "Have I said something that led you to believe otherwise?" "Did I leave the impression that . . .?" Do not accuse or judge. Try to focus on the problem itself rather than behavior and responses to those involved in the problem.

5. *Check whether your concept of the problem is valid for the other person.* "Is that the way you see it?" "Is your diagnosis the same as mine?"

6. *Be direct and leave no residual.* Once a joint diagnosis of the problem is established, be direct in expressing your feelings. The worst you can say is not as bad as the other person can imagine. Do not avoid the main issues. Be specific. Do not use a sweet smile to cloak angry feelings. Complete the confrontation so that there is no residual. Say all that you have to say. Express yourself so thoroughly and exhaustively that nothing remains to be said on that particular topic.

Organization

Regular classroom seating. Participants will be working with partners.

Equipment

None.

Instructions

"Look around the room. Select a person with whom, preferably, you have a real problem to discuss. If this is not possible, find a partner, and arbitrarily select a problem to discuss. Sit beside your partner and choose one of you to be No. 1. No. 1 will be the person who will attempt to express his feelings without hurting the other person. No. 2 can respond as seems appropriate. Let us follow the procedure which was outlined, one step at a time."

Activity

The participants attempt to carry out each step in order. When a step is completed by all members of the group, the instructor moves to the next step.

Instructions

1. One, examine your own feelings. Do you really want to hurt this person? If so, do not participate in the remainder of the exercise. We will discuss this at the end. Or you may talk with your partner about why and how you would like to hurt him.

"Now, the next step. Two, say something which acknowledges that there are two people and that two people are bound to have differences.

"Three, acknowledge the good will of the other person.

"Four, make a statement which indicates that the problem is separate from either of you, though it involves both of you.

"Five, ask whether the other person sees the problem in the same way you see it. Ask for feedback. Explore reactions.

"Six, be direct in describing and revealing your feelings. Say all you have to say. Leave nothing to be discussed at a later date."

Activity

Participants proceed step by step.

Instructions

"No. 2, please talk with No. 1 about how well he accomplished the process. Point out to him any of the procedures which he did not follow. Tell him what he did effectively. Explain if your feelings were or would have been hurt."

Activity

No. 2's give feedback on the procedures which were followed.

Instructions

"Now change partners with another couple, No. 1's pairing with No. 2's. Each couple should have one person who was a No. 1 and one person who was a No. 2.

"This time the No. 2's are to initiate the discussion. We will follow the same steps again, one at a time, in order.

"One, examine your feelings.

"Two, acknowledge that there are two people and that you are different.

"Three, acknowledge the good will of the other person.

"Four, indicate that the problem is a third thing, apart from either of you.

"Five, check whether your concept of the problem is valid for the other person.

"Six, be direct and leave no residual."

Activity

No. 2's follow the procedure. No. 1's give the feedback. The activity is continued with different partners until fifteen or twenty minutes before the end of the period. At that time, the leader conducts a summary discussion on the difficulties encountered in following the procedures.

UNIT III—DECISION MAKING

SESSION 1—THE DECISION-MAKING PROCESS

Theoretical Presentation

MAKING DECISIONS IS A process constantly required of people in the ordinary course of living.

We are accustomed to think that making decisions is an act that is good or bad, wise or foolish, destructive or rewarding—and an act in which one alternative is accepted and the other rejected.

This attitude presumes that there are only two alternatives—or a compromise between them. In a compromise, neither side gets what it really wants, since each side gives up something to the other.

It is not, in fact, necessary to have a winner and a loser. It is possible to make decisions in which each person gets enough of what he wants to satisfy him, and even most of what he may have wished. In the collaborative process, it is possible to make adjustments and alterations which enhance the gains and mitigate the losses for all concerned.

Increased understanding of communication involved in the collaborative processes can enable people to achieve their individual goals without forcing others to relinquish theirs. All factions gain concertedly.

Let us examine steps in the decision-making process and determine just how this type of inclusive amalgam may be accomplished.

1. *Try to define the problem.* The first task is to find the kernel of the problem, the critical factor. The inability to define the basic problem accurately and clearly is responsible for most poor decisions. A considerable amount of discussion of feelings

---

NOTE: This session is a lecture only, designed to set the stage for decision-making sessions which follow.

may be necessary to enable a person or persons to identify the problem. We somehow know we have found the kernel by a feeling of *having arrived,* of knowing there is nothing further to explore; it is a feeling of having reached *the bottom.*

Once the significant feelings have been discovered, it is then necessary to reconsider the goals or overall objectives to see whether or not achieving those goals would, in fact, adequately satisfy the feelings.

If the decision is to be ultimately satisfactory, it must be in harmony with our long-term goals, which may be multifarious. Consequently, all aspects of the goals must be held against the kernel of the problem so that we may see relationships between them.

Once the kernel has been discovered and has been held against the seemingly desired goals, the problem can then be separated into its various components or factors.

2. *Analyze yourself in relation to the problem.* Why is this particular situation a problem for you? What is it in your past experience which causes you to bring this particular problem into focus? Why, out of the myriads of problems available, have you selected this particular one? Why do you have an affinity for this problem?

3. *Collect facts related to the problem.* Facts relate to the past; decisions relate to the future. Whereas decisions are not merely a collection of facts, facts must be employed in making decisions. Facts help predict the results of future action and enable us to further refine our feelings in advance of action. It is also important to establish those areas where there is insufficient knowledge.

4. *Develop a wide range of alternative solutions, including no action.* Only a wide range of alternatives will enable a person to incorporate the best aspects of many solutions into the one choice he finally makes. The number of alternatives obviously varies with each problem, but one possible solution is common to all problems—to do nothing. To do nothing is a decision and should always be considered. Immediate or hasty decisions often preclude the development of sufficient alternatives and are especially likely to be imbued with assumptions and prejudices.

5. *Examine each alternative solution in the light of a number of different factors* (a) risks, (b) effort, (c) timing, (d) resources, (e) feelings and values, etc.

a. RISKS INVOLVED. What may be lost and what gained by choosing each alternative? Are the gains sufficient to justify the losses? How could the gains be magnified and the losses minimized?

b. EFFORT INVOLVED. What would be the easiest way to accomplish the desired result? Do some alternatives demand more effort than others? Would greater effort bring a greater gain?

c. TIMING. Is the time propitious to take the contemplated action? Would it be better to postpone action? For how long? When is the most convenient time? The most advantageous? Are convenience and advantage in conflict?

d. RESOURCES. Do you have the skill, the knowledge, the money to help carry out the proposed alternative? Do you have free choice among the alternatives, or are the resources weighted in favor of one alternative rather than another?

e. FEELINGS AND VALUES. Faced with a choice of options that involve personal values, a person has to know himself. Do the alternatives fit your real feelings? Try on each alternative for emotional size. If the alternatives will involve your doing more than you feel you should or need to do, you will probably feel anger. If you will be doing less than you feel you should do, you will probably feel guilt. If you feel uneasy about an alternative you have selected, you have probably failed to examine your emotions sufficiently.

Feelings as well as facts may be examined in relation to each of the above factors. An examination or anticipation of feelings in relation to each of the alternatives will assist in determining which is to be selected.

6. *Select a composite course of action which incorporates the best parts of each alternative and eliminates the worst parts of each alternative.* Do not select one alternative only, but incorporate various elements of risk, effort, timing, resources, feelings, and values into a satisfactory amalgam. Imagine the decision

being carried out and see how you will like it. Try to make a decision in which you can act as a person you would like. Try to make a decision you will like for a long time. Alter it if necessary to avoid anger or guilt. Decide exactly how much of each alternative you are willing to carry through without either too much anger or too much guilt.

If sufficient thought and feeling have gone into the decision in advance, it will not be necessary to worry unduly about the outcomes or engage in self-recriminating postmortems about the action which has been taken. Good decisions can be recognized by the sense of finality experienced at the time the decision is made, by the feeling of spontaneous freedom involved in taking the subsequent action, and by the absence of unanticipated consequences and the avoidance of unpleasant afterfeelings of regret, guilt, anger, or self-pity.

SESSION 2—AVOIDING THE PREMATURE DECISION:
YELLOW TICKETS FOR HASTE

Theoretical Presentation

The most common fault in decision-making is taking action before there has been adequate investigation of possible alternatives and adequate expression of feelings related to the various alternatives.

We will practice today to see if we can examine a problem, discuss it, and express feelings related to this problem without suggesting action of any kind or making a premature decision.

Organization

Chairs are pushed back against the wall so that participants are free to walk about in the room.

Equipment

Record player, a record of lively march music; tags of yellow construction paper, 2 x 3 in.; transparent tape.

Instructions

"I will play the music. When the music stops, you are to select a partner of your own sex. Imagine that you are going to take a one-week vacation with your partner. Talk with your partner about the kind of vacation you would enjoy most. Talk about any of the following factors (instructor lists the factors on the chalkboard):

1. Type of recreational activities available.
2. Money to be spent.
3. Work involved in making preparations—work that you are willing to do and work that you are not willing to do.
4. Amount of time involved.
5. Your health.
6. Preferred climate.
7. Preferred locale.
8. Type and degree of responsibility each person might have.
9. Your individual capabilities.
10. Your individual motivations.

11. Previous commitments.
12. Degree of change from your usual life style.
13. Other people who might be concerned.
14. Future consequences of the decision.

"As you are talking, discuss all aspects of each of the above topics. Discuss other subjects that are pertinent. Express any feelings you have.

"Do not make any decisions of any kind. Postpone any type of action. Don't say, 'Let's go Tuesday night and buy the tickets.' Do not suggest or propose any action. Do not make any decisions. *Merely talk* with your partner about all the factors involved. We will do this for ten minutes.

"If you catch your partner making a decision or suggesting definitive action, raise your hand. I will then come and attach a yellow tag to that person's shoulder. The purpose of the exercise is to see if you can finish the period without any yellow tags. Try to talk for the entire ten minutes."

Activity

The instructor plays the music. The participants move around the room until the music stops, when they select their partners. The pairs converse for ten minutes.

When a participant raises his hand, the instructor attaches a yellow tag to the shoulder of the one who has suggested action or made a premature decision.

At the end of ten minutes, the instructor plays the music again and the exercise is repeated with a new partner.

About fifteen minutes before the end of the period, the class is reassembled for summary discussion and acknowledgment of those who have avoided receiving a yellow ticket.

SESSION 3—THE FORCED CHOICE GAMBIT: WOULD YOU RATHER BE BEATEN ON TUESDAY OR ON THURSDAY?

Theoretical Presentation

Participation in making a decision involves participation in arriving at possible alternatives. The old saw, "Would you rather be beaten on Tuesday or on Thursday?" suggests the manipulative device which offers a person two apparent choices while offering him no real choice.

In the selling process, the most significant part is known as "the close." At this time the customer is on the verge of making a decision but is still undecided. The skillful salesman, aware of his client's tenuous indecision, offers a forced choice in which both alternatives involve purchase. "Would you rather pay cash or use our convenient easy-payment plan?"

Today we will practice resistance to the forced-choice gambit. Do you understand this concept? Who will be our first participant and begin the exercise?

Organization

Participants are seated in a circle or in concentric circles.

Equipment

None.

Instructions

"Our first volunteer will select someone in the class toward whom he will direct his question. This question will consist of a forced choice which hides a fundamental additional choice that is not stated. For instance, 'Let's go to the movies. Would you like to see *The Molly Coddler* or *Eat, Drink and Be Married?* The person questioned is not allowed to accept either of the choices offered but is to respond to the question related to the basic alternative. 'I would like to go to the movies, but I don't want to see either of those pictures. I want to see *Funny Boy*' or 'I don't especially want to go to the movies at all, but I would like to go for a walk.'

"If the person who answers manages to avoid the forced

choice, he takes his turn in proposing a forced choice to someone else. Does everyone understand the exercise? Do you have any questions?"

Activity

The first volunteer selects the one toward whom he wishes to direct his forced choice. If the recipient avoids the gambit, he is allowed to direct a forced choice to someone else. If he fails to avoid it, the first volunteer directs a forced choice to a different participant.

Participation is thus rotated throughout the group. No one can be selected as recipient who has been selected previously in the same exercise.

At the end of the period, the instructor conducts a discussion of the problems which have arisen during the exercise.

SESSION 4—WHEN YOU OFFER A CHOICE:
HALVING THE APPLE

Theoretical Presentation

A general principle which has been most helpful in setting up alternatives in stressful situations is proposed in a book entitled *How to Develop Your Executive Ability*:

> Cut the apple so accurately that you are willing to let the other person choose either half.[1]

The proposal is that when you offer someone a choice, you will not care which alternative the other person takes because the choices will be so carefully equated. Or if you are presented a situation to respond to, your choice of alternative responses will be such that either will be acceptable.

The principal advantage of attempting to slice the apple exactly in half is that in the process of trying to decide which are the equal halves, one is forced to examine all his own feelings regarding the problem.

Today we will try an experiment and see if we can learn to slice an apple exactly in half.

Organization

Regular classroom seating. Later the participants move their chairs so that they are divided into small groups.

Equipment

Pencil and paper, a penny; for each group, one slip of paper on which a specific situation has been prescribed, each situation embodying a request for a person to do something he really does not wish to do. The situation can be adapted to suit local conditions, customs, organizations and problems.

Instructions

"Divide into groups of three or four people. I am going to

NOTE: In the making of decisions, considering feelings before considering action is essential. This topic could easily span a number of sessions.

[1] Starch, Daniel: *How to Develop Your Executive Ability*, 7th ed. New York, Harper and Brothers, 1943, p. 202.

give each group a slip of paper on which a situation is described. This situation will be the topic of discussion for your group."

Activity

The instructor passes out to groups at random, slips of paper describing the following situations:

1. A neighbor who took care of your children while you were in the hospital asks you to serve as a volunteer in the Cancer Drive.

2. Your assistant minister's wife asks you to head the Program Committee of the P.T.A.

3. Your sister-in-law asks you to provide transportation for some members of her Cub Scout den for a field trip to a city ninety miles away.

4. A fellow worker, who was instrumental in getting you your job, asks you to be chairman of the decoration committee for the annual office party.

5. Your son's Scoutmaster asks you to give the inspirational at the annual meeting of the Rodeo Association.

6. Your brother, who is a lawyer, asks you to be host to a group of dignitaries who are surveying the law libraries in area colleges.

7. A former classmate asks you to give a tribute to the retiring principal at your fifteenth high school reunion. You recall that he was instrumental in your being suspended from school during the last two weeks of your senior year.

8. A co-worker asks you to be co-hostess at a bridal shower for a fellow office worker you dislike.

9. An old friend invites you to be a guest at the Emerald Charity Ball. You have been rejected three times when your name came up for membership in this organization.

10. You are called upon to frame a memorial tribute to a Sunday School class member whose personal and business ethics were, to your knowledge, unsavory.

11. A next-door neighbor gives your name as a character reference to the insurance company. This neighbor backed into your new Cadillac while intoxicated.

12. A distant relative sends you a wire to come at once to the bedside of a stricken aunt who has previously informed you that she has cut you out of her will.

13. While cleaning out your husband's desk drawer, you discover a packet marked "Cancelled Checks" and find that instead of checks it contains assorted souvenirs and pictures of his former secretary, now living in a distant city.

Instructions

"In each group you have a perplexing situation to deal with. By talking with each other, work out two alternative solutions to the problem, either of which you would be willing to accept. Draw half an apple on each side of your paper. Write one alternative in each half."

Activity

The groups try to develop equal alternatives. When all participants have apparently finished, the instructor uses the following procedures to check out the answers.

Instructions

"We are going to toss a coin to find out how you feel about your two alternative courses of action. The tossing of the coin is not to make the decision but to find out how you actually feel about the alternatives. When you examine your feelings about the fall of the coin, you will know more about your proposed response to the situation.

"Mark one half of the apple *heads*. Mark the other half *tails*. I am going to toss the coin. Let us imagine you will be expected to take the action which the coin indicates."

Activity

In each group, the halves of the apple are designated *heads* and *tails*. The instructor tosses the coin and announces how it falls.

Instructions

"Did you care at all how the flip of the coin turned out? If you had any feelings, either positive or negative, you failed to make the two sides of your apple even. Work on it some more, and make further adjustments in the alternatives until they are totally equivalent."

Activity

Participants in their groups discuss further in an attempt to make the alternatives equal.

Instructions

"Let us now hear what each group did with the problem. First, read your situation to the class. Then read what is written on each half of the apple and explain how you made the sides equivalent."

Activity

Each group in turn presents its report.

SESSION 5—MAKING A SOLITARY DECISION: WALKING THE TIGHTROPE BETWEEN ANGER AND GUILT

Organization

Groups are seated around tables.

Equipment

Strips of manila tag board, 36 in. long and 4 in. wide; marking pens; squares of red and purple construction paper, 2 x 2 in.; jars of rubber cement, paper and pencil.

Instructions

"In a situation requiring a given action, a certain amount of that action is optimum for one individual. When a person does more than he thinks he should, he will be angry. If he does less than he believes he should, he will feel guilty. Let us test this premise.

"We will first go through a practice situation. Imagine that your next-door neighbor asks you for a loan. I am going to name amounts of money. Here are some squares of red and purple paper. I will give each of you a square of each color. Purple stands for guilt. When I name an amount of money, wave your purple slip if you would feel guilty at refusing your neighbor an amount so small. Red stands for anger. If you would feel angry if you agreed to lend your neighbor an amount of money that large, wave your red slip of paper.

"Somewhere on the continuum there will be the right amount— neither too little nor too much. At that point, you probably won't feel much of anything. Somewhere near that point you will stop feeling guilty and will start feeling angry.

"I will name the amounts of the projected loan. At each number, wave one of your tags—the purple one if you would feel guilty and the red one if you would feel angry. Are there any questions? Let us try this.

"Ten cents, 25 cents, 50 cents, 1 dollar, 2 dollars, 3 dollars, 4 dollars, 5 dollars, 10 dollars, 15 dollars, 25 dollars, 50 dollars, 75 dollars, 100 dollars, 150 dollars, 200 dollars, 250 dollars, 300 dollars, 400 dollars, 500 dollars, 750 dollars, 1000 dollars, 2000 dollars, etc. (The instructor calibrates the amount of money according to the group. The first few numbers which are called should be clearly guilt-producing numbers. The last amounts should result in a display of anger tags only.)

"You now understand the principle. In decision-making, guilt changes to anger at a certain point along a continuum of alternatives.

"Now we shall apply the same principle to a problem of yours. Think about a problem about which you must make a decision.

"Develop five alternative solutions to this problem, including no action. All of the solutions should be of the same general type—that is, they should concern one variable: time, money, kinds of work, etc. Each of the five alternatives should be mutually exclusive, and each of the alternatives should be realistically possible. No alternative should be in the realm of fantasy or imagination. Each should be totally within your power to carry out. The solutions should not be contingent upon the actions of someone else.

"On the strips of manila tagboard I will give you, write the numbers 1, 2, 3, 4, and 5 across the top, while holding the paper horizontally. On your paper, write five alternative courses of action in your problem situation. Calibrate the five alternatives in order, naming the choice which would be the least drastic No. 1. Write alternative No. 1 on the left of the strip under the number 1. Place the alternative which would be the most drastic on the right under the number 5. Be sure to include *no action* as one alternative."

Activity

On their strips of cardboard, participants fill out five alternatives, arranged in a hierarchy.

Instructions

"Each of you put your strip of cardboard on the table in front of you. Put purple squares of paper opposite the alternatives which would make you feel guilty. If an action would make you feel extremely guilty, put a number of purple squares on it. Put red squares opposite the alternatives which would make you feel angry. If an alternative would make you very angry, put a number of red squares beside it."

Activity

Members of the class follow the directions. The instructor answers questions concerning procedure but refuses to answer questions concerning content.

Instructions

"Which of your alternatves would be the best to select? Which the worst? Would you rather feel anger or guilt?

"Now let us reconsider the concept of what we call the 'amalgam decision.' See if you can eliminate some of the factors which produce anger and guilt. Can you work out an alternative which incorporates some of the better aspects of other alternatives? Can you find an alternative that is better than any you have listed?

"Consider your problem again, from the point of view of time, money, personnel, transportation, work and effort, facilities, etc. See if you can reach a solution which would be better than any you have previously written."

"Those who have been able to work out some good alternatives, help those who are having difficulty. You may help each other in any way you can.

"Examine your best alternative again. Do you need to modify it to make it in line with your overall, long-term objectives for yourself? Can you carry out this alternative with peace of mind? Will there be any residual guilt or anger? Can you make further changes to eliminate any remaining anger or guilt?

"Now, select your best alternative, or incorporate the best parts of several solutions. Be sure your final alternative is guilt-free and anger-free.

"Would you like to try this exercise again next time with a different problem and a different set of alternatives?"

SESSION 6—MAKING A DUAL DECISION:
A NIGHT ON THE TOWN

Theoretical Presentation

Today we shall try to make a dual, or joint, decision. Whenever two people are involved, the decision-making process is likely to become even more complicated than when only one person is involved.

It is essential that there be adequate discussion of feelings before any action is taken. This is the first and most important principle. If decisions are made without sufficient discussion, both partners will harbor feelings that their opinions have been neither sought nor respected. Both will be dissatisfied with the decision, since there is no way it can accurately reflect their interests and desires. They will feel as though they have been required to stand aside and receive an edict.

You will therefore need to talk extensively about how you feel and what you want before you propose any action. Try to explore your partner's feelings. Try to continue discussion until you have reached an understanding eminently satisfactory to each person.

Bear in mind that both people must be active in making the dual decision. If one person removes himself from the problem and abdicates all responsibility, he creates a vacuum and forces the other person to make a decision. "Anything you want will be all right with me." The one thus forced to make the decision will resent the responsibility involved, and the one who abdicates it will feel martyred, victimized, or robbed of his "personality."

In today's exercise, make every effort to participate actively in the decision-making process. Do not passively leave the decision to the other person, under the guise of amiability. Do not "let things take their course."

Try to arrive at the amalgam-type decision described in previous lessons. Your aim will be to produce a situation in which each partner gets as much of what he wants as is feasible under the circumstances.

Do not compromise. If partners agree on the so-called compromise, each may subordinate his desires to those of the other, thinking that the other person is stating his real needs and interests. In most such cases, the final outcome will be something which neither partner wants.

Organization

Slips of paper are numbered 1,1; 2,2; 3,3; etc. The slips are shuffled and passed out at random without regard to sex. Those with the same number become partners and sit together.

Equipment

Numbered slips for dividing the group into pairs, pencil and paper for each pair.

Instructions

"We shall pretend that you two people are going out tonight. You have an automobile in good running condition and a full tank of gas. In addition, you have $3.35 in cash. Neither of you has any other money, nor can you spend any other money by using credit cards, borrowing money, or by using a similar device. You are to be gone from 7:00 P.M. until 11:00 P.M. You cannot leave earlier nor come home later. You are to use the entire four hours.

"Discuss and try to anticipate every issue which may arise. When you have finished making all decisions related to your evening together, write your decisions on the paper."

(The instructor can make the amount of money and the time involved appropriate to the setting. The money should not be sufficient to make possible the usual recreational activities, in order that ingenuity will be required.)

Activity

Pairs discuss the problem and write their conclusions. When all have finished, the instructor conducts a discussion.

Questions for Discussion

1. What kinds of difficulties did you experience in attempting to make a decision?
2. Did you develop a wide range of alternatives?
3. Were you able to talk extensively about your feelings related

to each alternative before decisions and actions were proposed?

4. Were both of you equally active in the process?
5. Did either of you agree to do something you would not really enjoy? If so, how did this agreement come about?
6. Was any difficulty avoided because you happened to be paired with someone whose interests were exactly like yours? Are you actually as much alike as it appeared?
7. Did you finally compromise in such a way that neither of you would honestly enjoy the evening?

SESSION 7—MAKING THE SMALL-GROUP DECISION:
1000 DOLLARS TO SPEND

Theoretical Presentation

You have worked on arriving at a solitary decision by your-self. You have worked on making a decision with one other person. Now let us consider the process of reaching a decision with a small group.

The plan for making a decision in a small group is basically similar to that used in making a dual decision. However, the more people involved, the more feelings there are involved. The more people involved, the less intimate the situation and the more reluctant people are to reveal their true feelings.

Organization

Participants are seated in groups of four or five, around tables.

Equipment

Paper and pencil for each group.

Instructions

"Here is your problem. You are in.....(place).....on this day, the......(number).......day of.......(month)......., ...(year)..... You have been living in a house with the other people in your group. Your house has just burned to the ground, destroying everything you own. You are left with nothing except the clothes you are presently wearing. You have an insurance check for 1000 dollars. You are all at present un-employed, and you are not allowed to seek financial help from relatives, friends, or welfare. You have no savings, no stocks and bonds, no credit cards. There is no other source of money. All you have, unless you earn it, is 1000 dollars.

"From this moment on, your fate is the fate of the others in your group. The solution must be one which includes all of

NOTE: The decision-making process becomes still more complicated when a number of people are involved. The discussion in this session could easily span overnight, a weekend, or a number of sessions. The instructor should press for serious consideration of the decisions involved. Participants have a tendency to agree too quickly and too easily.

you together. Your solution must be for your common problem. Aim for the greatest degree of satisfaction to all members of your group.

"To arrive at your group decision, follow the procedure written on the board:

1. Define and limit the problems of time, money, personnel, transportation, weather, effort, facilities, etc.
2. Analyze the problems. Who shall be consulted? Who informed? What data are needed? What data are missing?
3. Develop alternative solutions. Examine all possibilities, including no action. Write possible alternatives on your paper.
4. Each of you should express all the feelings you have regarding all alternatives, including an individual affirmation as to which alternative would best meet your needs.
5. Each of you should discuss feelings related to individual statements made by others.
6. Write your group consensus of what will best meet the needs of all members.
7. Each of you should try to respond with your feelings about the group consensus. Do not abnegate your desires completely. The group consensus as to action should contain something related to the needs of each of you.
8. After each of you has expressed his feelings, reconsider the group consensus if necessary. Change as needed whatever you have written.
9. Discuss the action required to implement the consensual decision, including relevant details. Put into writing the action to be taken.
10. Delegate responsibilities for carrying out the action. Specifically assign responsibility for each part of the action.
11. Check with each person in the group to see if there exist any residual feelings concerning the whole problem and the proposed solutions.

"Are there any questions concerning the procedure? If further questions arise, I will try to answer them if they relate to procedure. I cannot help you with your decisions."

Activity

Groups meet and discuss their problem and their solutions. At the end of the period, the leader conducts a discussion of the process involved in reaching a group decision.

Questions for Discussion
1. Were you satisfied with the outcome?
2. Did you become confused in following the process? How? At what point?
3. Were you aggressive or passive in the decision-making process?
4. Would you be satisfied six months from now with your decisions? A year from now? Five years from now?

UNIT IV—MAXIMS FOR PROBLEM SOLVING

THE FOLLOWING ARE some guidelines for solving problems.

1. *Acknowledge that problem solving is a process, usually slow.* Problems evolve through a process and are solved by a process. The acceptance of problems as processes means searching for processes as solutions to problems. It is futile to seek single "solutions" for such generalized problems as "getting well." Acceptance that problem solving is a process leads to the acceptance of small changes as evidence of the process, and consequently of progress.

Our language is full of process words which suggest the ways in which problems may be altered. By examining some of these words, we can obtain clues to approaching problems: to abate, to diminish, to enhance, to limit, to modify, to reinforce, to qualify, to mitigate, to restrain, to curtail, to dodge, to rescind, to transform, to yield, to abridge, to extend, to accede, to interpose, to juxtapose, to accelerate, to decelerate, to tighten, to relax, to dilute, to concentrate. *When talking about a problem, or thinking about a solution, use process words.*

2. *Try to avoid escalating the problem.* Stop whatever identifiable action precipitated the problem, and continue to avoid such action. Repetitive action not only invites repetitive consequences but worse consequences.

3. *Seek self-knowledge.* Since each person is himself a major factor in the creation of the problem he experiences, problem solving depends on self-knowledge and self-alteration. Self-knowledge enables us to establish suitable priorities, distinguishing between important and unimportant decisions and giving appropriate attention to each.

Explore your potential capacities and seek productivity that is suitable for your potential. Many people strive for wholly

---

NOTE: This session is a summary lecture. Each point may be discussed.

unrealistic goals. To whatever extent we understand our capacities, our limitations, and our liabilities, we are able to set goals in reasonable consonance with our capabilities.

4. *Beware of escape devices.* All of us utilize multifarious escape devices, some direct and some indirect, some active and some passive. Certain avoidances wholly ignore reality and only serve to confuse the issue. "My mother would know what to do in this situation if she were living today."

Taking action may, in itself, be a means of avoidance. "Let's drop the argument and go shopping together." Action is no substitute for incompleted discussion of feelings.

5. *Avoid bipolar thinking.* Bipolar thinking makes one prey to the trap: "If I can't have everything I want, I don't want anything." A person who thinks in terms of only two alternatives can never understand his problem, since all problems are multicausal and therefore offer multifaceted solutions. At best, we human beings see only a small portion of any problem and consider only a few of the countless alternative solutions.

6. *Anticipate future feelings, before taking action.* We spend much time expressing feelings engendered by past actions, but the really productive talk is that which relates to feelings predictable under certain future conditions. Discussion should precede action, not follow it. Such talk makes possible the alteration of a future situation.

Anticipating future feelings requires anticipating the future situation in specific detail: place, time, context, people. Project your feelings in advance; imagine how you will feel. Face the situation realistically in your imagination; the real time then becomes the second time, and having faced it before, you will find it far less frightening.

7. *Do not wrestle with huge, comprehensive, overwhelming problems.* For expressive purposes, feelings must be small, manageable, and limited to specific places and specific times under specific conditions. Do not begin to learn expressiveness in situations that demand sophisticated expressive skill.

Approach with circumspection any situation known to be emotionally painful. Attempt to alleviate the difficulty by taking advance action which will place the emotional problem within the range of your expressive ability.

8. *Confine yourself to expressing your own feelings.* Express your own feelings and let others express theirs. If your goal is to communicate, you must not circumscribe the feelings of others by saying, "You have no right to feel that way." Neither should you allow others to define your rights in regard to feelings.

9. *Confine your expression to feelings pertinent to the situation at hand.* Today's feelings will present an entirely adequate sample of all your feelings; it is not necessary to introduce feelings from past situations. "You forgot our anniversary the first year we were married. It hurts me every time I think of it."

10. *In one-to-one relationships, keep your expressions on a one-to-one basis.* Introducing opinions of others to support your own point of view is an indirect means of breaking off relatedness. Do not bolster your arguments by adding the evidence or opinions of others: "Experts say my way is right." "All those in the club agree with me." "Your mother sees it my way."

11. *Stay related to the people involved in the situation.* Resolution of interpersonal problems must be achieved through interpersonal solutions. Breaking off relatedness cannot solve problems of relatedness. People possess different values. Your point of view cannot—and indeed does not need to—always coincide with the point of view held by others.

On occasion it may be necessary to acknowledge that all efforts at reconciliation have resulted in failure and that differences are irreconcilable. For example, divorce is an acknowledgment of failure in marital relatedness; however, divorce cannot conceivably be viewed as a *solution* to a problem.

Whenever possible, deal directly with those involved in the problem. Once cognizant of a problem, apprise those involved that you are concerned. Early communication can avert the need for crisis communication. If you cannot deal directly with those involved, you will need to seek outside professional help.

12. *Be the active person in your own life.* Situations do not "work themselves out." Each person must participate actively in the direction of his own life if he wishes to enjoy self-esteem.

Section VI
Toward Maturity

UNIT I—OWNERSHIP OF FEELINGS

SESSION 1—FEELINGS ABOUT OWNERSHIP

Theoretical Presentation

IN ORDER TO understand ownership, let us examine those things which we own and invest with importance. Let us look at what we do with these things and consider the feelings and attitudes we have about these possessions. Possibly by doing so, we can understand something of the meaning of ownership.

Organization

Regular classroom seating.

Equipment

Paper and pencil for each participant.

Instructions

"Write your name in the top right-hand corner of your paper. I am going to ask you a number of questions. Copy the question on your paper, and after each question, write your answer. When you have finished writing, divide into small groups of four or five. In your groups, discuss your answers to each of the questions. Compare your reactions with those of others in the group."

Questions to be Answered

1. What is the most important *thing* that you own? It must be tangible; it cannot be an idea, a concept, an abstraction or a symbol.
2. What positive feelings do you have about owning it? Obviously, if it is the most important thing you own, it will be something about which you have many feelings. All of us have positive and negative feelings about almost everything. What positive feelings do you have about this thing you own?
3. What negative feelings do you have about this thing?

223

4. What do you have to do to keep it?
5. How would you feel if you lost part of it?
6. How would you feel if you lost all of it?

Activity

Participants write answers to the questions. When the writing is completed, they meet in groups and discuss their answers to the questions. If preferred, the instructor can duplicate the collated answers and distribute them to the groups for discussion the succeeding period. In this way, each person is given an opportunity to see and discuss the answers given by all participants in the class.

Response of the Pilot Group: Quotations from Participants

THINGS I OWN THAT ARE IMPORTANT TO ME

Item	Frequency of Mention	Item	Frequency of Mention
Car	9	Trilobite	1
Wedding ring	4	Set of dentures	1
Other ring	3	Horse	1
House	3	Air-conditioning	1
Wedding pictures	2	Apartment	1
Sewing machine	2	Clothes	1
Books	2	Diploma	1
Stereo	2	Poodle dog	1
Real estate	2	Basketball trophy	1
Oil leases	2	Watch	1
Piano	2	Cat	1
Chain with bells on it	1	Music	1
Pictures of me with someone	1	Jewelry	1
Records	1	Calf	1
Hand-made silk shirt	1		

Positive Feelings about Ownership

"Of all my things like it, it is the best I have."
"I am glad it is paid for."
"I like its color, its convenience, its easy handling, its luxury."
"It meets my needs."
"I feel pleasure in enjoying it, looking at it."
"It is esthetically satisfying."
"I like it because I could not do other things without it."
"It brings me money."

"I designed and decorated it."

"It expresses me; it makes me feel confident."

"It gives me a good feeling of accomplishment, of individuality, of choice, of belonging, of pride."

"I feel sentimental and nostalgic about it. It brings back memories of warmth and joy."

"It reminds me of someone who has died."

"It came as a reward for something I had done."

"I feel free and secure when I use it. It relieves my tension."

"I enjoy being known as the person who owns it. I bask in others' admiration of it. It gives me status."

"It makes me feel showy, sexy, wicked, superior."

"I enjoy increasing its beauty."

Negative Feelings about Ownership

"I feel responsible. Taking care of it becomes a pressure and a burden, and I become annoyed."

"It is a frightful expense. It costs so much to operate."

"It requires work. It gets dirty and deteriorates if not repaired."

"I have to wind it every day or it will not run."

"Only experts can take care of its necessities."

"Sometimes it is too small and has to be enlarged."

"Sometimes it gets too tight and has to be stretched."

"Sometimes it gets sick at inconvenient times."

"Sometimes it escapes and I can't find it."

"Through it, I avoid communication. I withdraw, forget my responsibilities and retreat to loneliness."

"Sometimes I don't like it when I know I should."

"I feel guilty when I mangle it, and frustrated when I am inept and can't use it as well as I would like to."

"It frightens me because it expresses too closely what I feel, hope, and dream."

What I Have to Do to Keep What I Own

"I have to take responsibility for it. I have to pay money to maintain it. I have to obtain insurance, registration, license plates."

"I have to treasure it, protect it from loss, fire and theft. I have to protect it from wear, give it water, and keep it filled with fuel."

"I have to do the work involved to keep it in safe running order, since it requires maintenance and upkeep."

"I straighten it daily, clean it thoroughly once a week and paint it every three or four years."

"I keep fluff from around the mechanism, have it tuned, change the filter, replace broken or damaged parts."

"I have conferences about it, listen to comments on it, revise the methods of working with it which do not work. I need to continue study and work to keep abreast with it."

"I have to get along with the other people involved in order to keep it. I have to teach others how to use it properly."

How I Would Feel If I Lost All or Part of What I Own

"First, I would feel a void. I would be stunned and have no feeling. I would feel lonely, lost, and desolate."

"I would feel uncomfortable, uneasy, frightened."

"I would feel outraged and cheated."

"I would be embarrassed having to tell others I had lost it."

"I would feel guilt that I had not been strong enough or good enough to maintain it."

"It would seem irreplaceable. I would hate having to get along with something less adequate."

"All my pleasures and enjoyments would be diminished."

"The value in its intactness would be gone."

"I wouldn't be able to do what I had done."

"If what was left was any good, I would repair it. If I could not repair it, I would try to replace it with something similar."

"It might not be so bad to get a new start. It would be a mental rebirth."

SESSION 2–OWNERSHIP OF FEELINGS: A VISIT
TO THE NOTARY PUBLIC

Theoretical Presentation

(The instructor writes the following quotation on the chalkboard.)

> Property is the right to possess, use, enjoy, and dispose of land and other things; it is not only the right to use but also *to bar others from the use thereof.*[1]

We ordinarily apply the term *ownership* to possessions only—almost never to ideas, concepts, or other abstractions. Today we will examine ownership of feelings, since this ownership is related to expressiveness.

In the previous lesson we examined the enjoyment and pleasure derived from ownership of property. We also examined the annoyance and responsibility related to care, maintenance, usage, and protection of our possessions. Finally, we examined the feelings related to loss of part or all of what is owned. We found that loss produces discomfort, uneasiness, guilt, and desolation. We further discovered that if a person loses property he really cares about, he affirms his need for it by replacement if it is lost or destroyed, or by repairing it if it is damaged.

Carl Rogers has stated that a person can express any feeling he is willing to own.[2]

If feelings are owned with the same degree of possessiveness that personal property is owned, we have the right to display feelings, use feelings, enjoy feelings, and dispose of feelings. It is not only our right to use our own feelings for our own purposes but to bar others from using our feelings for their purposes. It is also presumed that our rights concerning the feelings of others become curtailed if we infringe upon their property.

Organization

Regular classroom seating. At the front of the room there

---

[1] Masteller, Kenneth C.: How to avoid financial tangles. *Economic Education Bulletin,* 7:1, 1967, p. 5.

[2] Rogers, Carl: Lecture: "My Way of Facilitating a Group." Fourth Annual Institute for Psychiatric Education, Dallas, Dallas League of Nurses and Timberlawn Foundation, Dallas, March 30, 1969.

is a small desk with a teller's wicket bearing a sign, *Notary Public*. The instructor will subsequently preside in this kiosk, playing the role of Notary Public, witnessing and sealing the signed warranty deeds.

Equipment

Paper and pencil, one copy of the *Warranty Deed to Feelings* for each participant, pens, material to make a small teller's wicket for the Notary, Notary Public sign; gold notary seals, one for each contract (Denison Notarial Seals, No. 32-321 (4521)); blue legal document covers into which the Notary can place the *Warranty Deed to Feelings* after it has been notarized. The provision of such covers will lend dignity to the proceedings, but covers are not essential.

Instructions

"Today we will work in groups of four or five. Your discussion will be centered about ownership of feelings and its meaning. Select a group recorder who will set down the main points of your discussion."

Activity

Participants form into groups and discuss the following questions for approximately twenty minutes.

Questions for Discussion

1. What does it mean to own feelings?
2. What is the difference between accepting a feeling and owning it?
3. Are *you* willing to own *your* feelings?
4. What methods do you use to avoid ownership of feelings?
5. Are you willing to own all kinds of feelings?
6. What benefits are derived from ownership of feelings? What benefits are lost if you are unwilling to own your feelings?

Response of the Pilot Group: Collation

To avoid ownership, I can deny or hide my feelings. I can pretend I don't own them. I can give them away. I can say they do not belong to me; they belong to someone else.

I can ignore them. I can pretend they do not exist.

I can acknowledge that I have them, but say I can't help it: The power to divest myself of ownership is not within me.

I can lose them by not defending ownership.

I can take no responsibility. I can realize that I have a feeling and say, "That's how I am." This is acceptance. It does not call for any action.

Ownership is different from acceptance. If I own a feeling, I take responsibility for it; I am prepared to develop it, repair it, improve it, replace it, or abandon it. Ownership calls for action, for work.

Acceptance gives awareness but not identity. Ownership is a source of identity—of self-confidence.

Instructions

"To culminate our discussion today, we are going to participate in a quasi-legal ritual. You are going to deed your feelings to yourselves.

"If you own property, you usually have acquired it by a warranty deed. Another person deeds the property to you, and you then become the owner. Today you are going to make public acknowledgment of ownership of your feelings by signing a deed to your feelings in the presence of two witnesses.

"For these purposes, I have prepared a document entitled *Warranty Deed to Feelings*. (The instructor passes out a copy of the deed to each participant.) Each of you will fill out one of these deeds. First of all, fill in your name as Grantor. Then list the feelings you are conveying to yourself. Do not cite a general feeling, such as *love*. Be very specific. Specify the object of your feeling and the limits of circumstances and time.

"For example, '. . . the following personal feelings, to-wit: My anger at my husband on Sunday afternoons between 2 P.M. and 4 P.M. when he watches the football game on television instead of doing something with me and the children.'

"Each of you proceed now to fill out, in pen, your *Warranty Deed to Feelings*. When you have completed it by filling in all the blanks, come with two witnesses to the office of the Notary

Public. You will sign the deed before the Notary to declare that you have executed the instrument for the purposes and considerations therein expressed. You will be expected to produce some identification. The witnesses will sign to show that they saw you sign your name. The Notary Public will notarize your document.

"Are there any questions? If not, proceed with your deeds. Be careful to limit the boundaries of your feelings as to time, place, and circumstances in which they arise."

Activity

Each participant fills out his deed. When he has completed it, he finds two others to serve as witnesses and appears at the office of the Notary Public to have his document notarized.

Even though he knows the principal well, the Notary asks for identification with great solemnity. Principal and witnesses sign the deed in the designated places, and the Notary notarizes the document by filling in the date, signing in the appropriate blank, and affixing the gold seal. He also encloses the deeds in the blue cover and inscribes a title on the front of the cover. He returns the signed document to the owner.

When all documents have been notarized, the class is dismissed without further comment.

WARRANTY DEED TO FEELINGS

Know All Men By These Presents:

That I, ..., Grantor, do hereby grant, bargain, sell and convey unto myself, Grantee, and unto my heirs and assigns forever, the following described personal feelings, to-wit:

....

....

....

Grantee covenants to keep these feelings adequately insured against loss or damage, to pay all taxes levied upon them and all indebtedness secured by mortgage lien thereon, and to maintain and keep the feelings in good condition and repair.

Grantee covenants to defend the title to said feelings against all lawful claims whatsoever.

Witness my hand at ...., ...,
          (city)   (state)

this .... day of ...., 19.........

                                                        (L.S.)
                                          ....
                                                    Grantor

....
          Witness

....
          Witness

ACKNOWLEDGMENT

State of ....
County of ....

On this .... day of ...., 19......., before me, a notary public, appeared ...., to me well known, who acknowledged that .... had executed the foregoing instrument for the consideration and purposes therein set forth.

                                          ....
                                                Notary Public

Seal

UNIT II—MAKING CHOICES AND ESTABLISHING PRIORITIES

SESSION 1—GOAL SETTING: ALICE AND THE CHESHIRE CAT

Alice asked the Cheshire Cat, "Would you tell me, please, which way I ought to walk from here?"

"That depends a good deal on where you want to get to," said the Cat.

"I don't care much where . . ." said Alice.

"Then it doesn't matter which way you walk," said the Cat.[1]

Theoretical Presentation

(The instructor reads the above quotation.)

U NLESS WE KNOW where we want to get to, it makes little difference which direction we go. Conversely, we must decide where we want to get to if we want our own direction to make a difference. We can derive a sense of accomplishment only from achieving a goal we set before we start going toward it. If we do not set the goal in advance, we cannot enjoy its attainment.

As long as we drift through life like flotsam and jetsam tossed by each passing wave, we can experience no sense of accomplishment. We derive only limited satisfaction from the accomplishment of goals set for us by others. Our own goals need not be unique or vastly different from the goals of others, but self-confidence comes from participation in the selection of the goal and from our self-directed efforts to accomplish what we set out to do.

Organization

Regular classroom seating.

Equipment

Paper and pencil for each participant.

NOTE: The shock ending is especially startling to those unwilling to invest in goal setting.

[1] Carroll, Lewis: *Alice in Wonderland.*

Instructions

"Our topic for today is goal setting, a most important topic. The lesson is an exacting one. You will have to follow the instructions precisely to be able to benefit from the lesson.

"Leave your chair and form into groups of three. Do not include in the group anyone who was originally sitting near you. Be sure you have *three* people in your group.

"Write your name in the top right-hand corner of the paper. Now write one goal for one definite period of time: a day, a week, a month. After you have written your goals, discuss them in your groups."

Activity

The instructor reads the specific instructions carefully but makes no comment if participants fail to get into groups as designated. They work for ten or fifteen minutes discussing and writing down their goals.

Instructions

"Those of you who are not in a group of three, tear up your papers. I pointed out to you that goal setting was an important topic and that an understanding of the lesson depended on following the instructions carefully. If you did not bother to get into groups of three, you have shown that you do not care sufficiently about goal setting. Your goals can therefore be of little importance."

Response of the Pilot Group: Instructor's Observations

Participants who worked alone, along with those who were in groups of two or of four or more, reluctantly and angrily destroyed the sheets of paper on which they had written their goals. Many made excuses and protested unfairness.

Instructions

"Those of you who failed to leave your chairs and are still occupying the same chair you chose when you came into class today, tear up your papers. You were instructed to leave your chair. You are too lazy or too passive to accomplish any of the goals you have devised, so it really makes no difference what they are. Tear up your paper."

Response of the Pilot Group: Instructor's Observations

After further loud protests, those who had not moved from their original chairs tore up the papers on which they had written their goals.

Instructions

"How many are left who still have papers? Bring them to the center here and form a circle. Those of you with papers will talk as a group about your goals. Those of you who have torn up your papers, move to the outside. It will not be possible for you to participate in the discussion. Since you no longer have any goals yourself, you cannot contribute to the discussion of the goals of others."

Activity

Those who still have papers conduct a discussion. Those without papers sit around the outside as silent nonparticipants. The following questions are discussed in turn:

Questions for Discussion

1. Is the goal attainable?
2. How will you know when you have reached the goal?
3. Have you made a realistic assessment of yourself? Of other people? Of circumstances in the environment?
4. What are the assets you have to mobilize in your efforts to reach the goal?
5. Which of your faults could hinder your progress toward the goal you have set? How can you minimize your obstacles?

Activity

Either during this or a succeeding lesson, the participants forced to tear up their papers should be given an opportunity to ventilate their feelings, since this action is likely to produce a great deal of anger.

Optional Supplement

The following assignment may be given and discussed during the next period if it seems that further discussion of specific goal setting would be helpful.

"Put your name on the top of another sheet of paper. Now write a goal which you can accomplish before the next meeting of the class. At that time we will have a report on whether you accomplished the goal you set for yourself. I will hold the papers on which you have written your goal so that we can check it against your accomplishment."

SESSION 2—MAPPING THE ROUTE

> First say to yourself what you would be; and then do what you
> have to do.
>
> EPICTETUS, Circa 60 A.D.

Organization

Regular classroom seating.

Equipment

Black felt-tipped marker for the instructor; pencils, 8½ x 14 in.;
mimeographed sheets divided into vertical and horizontal
columns, as shown in the sample.

Instructions

"Write your name in the upper right-hand corner of the paper.
In vertical column 1 "What I Am" and horizontal column 1 "My
Capabilities," write your present capabilities. In horizontal
column 2 set down your present skills and knowledge. In column
3, cite your present feelings. In vertical column 2 write what
you would like to be in terms of capabilities, skills and knowledge,
and feelings. Try to write something in all twelve boxes."

Activity

Participants fill out the paper. When they have finished
writing, the instructor asks questions which they attempt to check
against what they have written. The questions serve to help
each participant improve his paper to the best of his ability.
Items may be rewritten as necessary in response to the questions.

Questions for Consideration by Individuals

1. Is what you have put down within your power to do, or does
   its accomplishment depend on someone else?
2. Is what you have put down something you are actually willing
   to do or are you merely exhorting yourself to do something
   you honestly have no intention of doing?

NOTE: The shock consequences of this session startle those who are unwilling
to participate in a reciprocal communicative process. The session properly spans
two periods, since it is necessary for the instructor to correct the papers.

MY GOALS

	What I Am	What I Would Like to Be	What I Need to Do to Become What I Would Like to Be	What I Am Doing Today to Become What I Would Like to Be
My Capabilities				
My Skills and Knowledge				
My Feelings				

3. Is your goal something that has an end, a terminal point at which you can say, "I have now accomplished my goal?"
4. Have you included some practical and immediate steps with which to begin attainment of your goal?
5. Is your name on your paper? Are you willing to make a public declaration of the goal you have set for yourself?

Instructions

"If you have answered these questions to your satisfaction, we can proceed to the next step.

"Imagine that you are in one long line. (The instructor indicates the direction in which papers are to be passed.) Pass your paper to the next person ahead of you in line. Read the paper you receive, then pass it on to the next person. If at any time you would like to give a written response to the writer of the paper, do so on the back of the sheet. If you write something, sign your name to the comment. You are not allowed to give anonymous responses."

Activity

Participants pass papers around, and each reads the goals of all the others. Each writes comments as desired. At the end of the period, the instructor collects the papers.

After the class and before the next class meeting, the instructor goes over the papers, listing names of people who have made comments to others on the backs of the sheets. Many participants will give responses to others, but some probably will give no responses. On the backs of the papers of those who gave no responses, the instructor blacks out all the responses received, so that they are no longer readable. For this purpose, the felt-tipped marking pen is used.

The papers are returned the following period. Those who gave responses to others have an opportunity to read the responses to their goals. Those who gave no responses find the comments on their papers have been blacked out. When they ask the instructor why their feedback has been obliterated, the instructor answers, "Because communication is a two-way process. If you give no response to others, you cannot expect to get any yourself."

SESSION 3—PRIORITY

Organization
Regular classroom seating.

Equipment
Paper and pencil for each participant.

Instructions
"Today we will have a brief review on choice, which we have discussed fully under "Decision Making" and "Goal Setting." Following the review, we will discuss priority.

"Our review will take the form of a responsive reading. First, I will read a statement. You will insert your own name, and repeat the statement, in unison. If my statement offers a choice, you will insert your own name, select one of the alternatives, and repeat that part only. If the statement you select suggests action, you will perform the action as indicated while repeating the statement."

Activity: Responsive Reading
The instructor and the group participate in the following responsive reading, according to the directions specified.

I Choose

Instructor: My name is (*instructor names himself*).
Group: My name is (*each person fills in his name*).
Instructor: I am a human being.
Group: I am a human being.
Instructor: Some things in my environment I *can* control.
Group: Some things in my environment I *can* control.
Instructor: Some things in my environment I *cannot* control. I can do nothing about contingency.
Group: Some things in my environment I *cannot* control. I can do nothing about contingency.
Instructor: What I *can* control in my environment is my own behavior.
Group: What I *can* control in my environment is my own behavior.

Instructor: I, (*instructor names himself*), walk. (Instructor walks.)

Group: I, (*each person names himself*), walk. (Each person walks.)

Instructor: I, (*instructor names himself*), choose to walk rather than sit. (walks)

Group: I, (*each person names himself*), choose to walk rather than sit. (all walk)

Instructor: I, (*instructor names himself*), choose to sit rather than walk. (sits)

Group: I, (*each person names himself*), choose to sit rather than walk. (all sit)

Instructor: Now I will offer you alternatives. Choose and repeat one of the alternatives. Do the suggested action.

I choose to keep my hands folded.

I choose to raise my arms over my head.

Group: (Each participant selects one of the alternatives, repeats the statement aloud and takes the action suggested in the statement.)

I choose to.......................

Instructor: I choose to nod my head and smile at my neighbor.

I choose to bow my head and look sad.

Group: I choose to.......................

Instructor: I choose to rise and talk to my neighbor.

I choose to sit in my chair and say nothing.

Group: I choose to.......................

Instructor: I choose to talk with many people in the room.

I choose to talk with only one person in the room.

I choose to talk with no one.

Group: I choose to.......................

Instructor: I like myself best when I talk to many people in the room.

I like myself best when I talk with only one person in the room.

I like myself best when I talk to no one.

Group: I like myself best when.......................

(Each participant selects the statement applicable to himself.)

Instructor: I, (*instructor names himself*), can choose to be the kind of person I will like.

Group: I, (*each person names himself*), can choose to be the kind of person I will like.

Instructor: If I choose my behavior, I can become a person worthy of my own esteem.

Group: If I choose my behavior, I can become a person worthy of my own esteem.

Instructor: If I choose behavior I consider worthy, then I, (*instructor names himself*), will have self-esteem.

Group: If I choose behavior I consider worthy, then I, (*each person names himself*), will have self-esteem.

Theoretical Presentation

Choosing to do something must involve choosing not to do something else. If you choose to go to the movies tonight, you also choose not to remain home and watch television. Affirmation is sometimes easier than negation. Forbearance is sometimes easier than action, sometimes more difficult. Both courses are part of choosing. Self-esteem is a byproduct of choice.

It is not enough, however, to choose what one will do and what one will not do. It is also necessary to choose what will be done first, what will receive priority. Priority has to do with precedence, that is, what we put first either in point of time or in importance. Whatever we put first, we consequently endow with greatest importance, since other persons, situations or actions necessarily yield to that priority. The goal or action that is so significant that all other goals or actions must yield to it is the goal which has priority. The prime time, the most time, the first time must go to that which commands the greatest priority. When a choice of goals is required, precedence goes to the goal which has been given highest priority.

> This above all: to thine own self be true,
> And it must follow, as the night the day,
> Thou canst not then be false to any man.
>
> *Hamlet*, Act 1, Sec. 3, Line 75

"This above all" is a statement of priority. Upon the completion of Number One, other items begin to fall into their appropriate places. When a person has chosen his number-one priority, the other aspects of his life immediately become subordinate and capable of being assigned to a proper rank. When he places priorities on his goals, his confusion begins to dissipate and he is able to gain perspective. Since he has taken a further step in the determination of his own course of living, he experiences an increased measure of self-esteem.

Instructions

"On your paper, write your name in the upper right-hand corner. Then determine and write five goals for yourself that you could accomplish within one year from today.

"Now rank these goals from one to five, marking as *Number One* the goal you would put first—the one which would take precedence over all others and to which you would give the greatest time and effort. It should be the goal you would start to accomplish before you begin working toward any of the other goals listed. Continue ranking the other goals in the order of their importance and primacy."

Activity

Participants list their goals and attempt to assign priorities to them. When they have finished writing, they discuss difficulties encountered in attempting to assign priorities.

UNIT III—SELECTING THE ACTION: EROS AND THANATOS

I find an ultimate value in the efforts of human beings to do more than merely exist, to choose and analyze their experiences and by the findings of that analysis help themselves to further experiences which are of a more pleasurable kind. I use the word pleasurable in its widest sense; to describe such experiences as come from good food and wine, exercise, and the physical act of lovemaking, the practice of a beloved craft or art or science, a happy marriage, the care of children or the sick or the old by those who enjoy it, the service of valid ideas, or the administration of worthy institutions, or the pursuit of agreeable sensations.[1]

Theoretical Presentation

MENNINGER SUGGESTS THAT there are three basic ways in which to alter the forces of hate within oneself:[2]

1. Diminish the aggressive element.
2. Diminish the self-punitive element.
3. Enhance the erotic element.

All of us have at our disposal a given amount of time and a somewhat limited choice as to the type of activities we will engage in. Within these limits, we do have a choice as to what type of action we will take in any situation.

Those activities which build and create life, which give life, sustain life or protect life, we shall call "Eros activities." Those which destroy life, tear down life, diminish life, or activities which waste or vandalize, we shall call "Thanatos activities." Aggressive energies may therefore be directed toward love or toward death.

First, aggressive energy may be harnessed by exercising

---

[1] Menninger, Karl: *Love Against Hate*. New York, Harcourt, Brace and World, 1942, p. 292.

[2] Menninger, Karl A.: *Man Against Himself*. New York, Harcourt Brace, 1938, p. 421-442.

restraint—by refraining from activities which are destructive. Restraint may be either physical or psychological. By exercising restraint and not doing something which is harmful to his health, a person who gives up smoking is choosing a life force rather than a death force.

Second, aggressive energy may be dispelled by displacing it from people to more appropriate, less destructible targets. This is called *catharsis.*

> It is certainly more desirable for a man to pound a punching bag or walk miles in pursuit of a golf ball than to exert the same energy in attacking the reputation of his neighbor, the peace of mind of his wife, or the functioning of his own heart.[3]

Third, a person can engage in vigorous self-assertion, sufficient to keep others out of his life space. The normal activity necessary to maintain a well-defended place at home, at work, and in the community is itself sufficient to utilize a considerable amount of aggressive energy.

Fourth, a person can devote his aggressive energies to the improvement of his personal and social environment: his home, his community, his business, education, or politics. He can direct his aggression toward "ignorance, crime, vice, disease, poverty—and let us add ugliness, and even aggressiveness itself."[4]

Today we shall differentiate between Eros and Thanatos activities.

Organization

Circle or double circle with the chalkboard at one edge of the circle. The instructor stands or sits near the chalkboard.

Equipment

None.

Instructions

"We will classify activities into those concerned with things, those concerned with nature, those concerned with other people, and those concerned with ourselves. We will divide the board

---

[3] Menninger, Karl A.: *Man Against Himself. op. cit.,* p. 424.
[4] *Ibid.*

into two columns, labeling the column on the left "Eros" and the column on the right "Thanatos." We will limit activities first to those concerned with things, listing Eros and Thanatos activities."

Activity

Class members suggest Eros and Thanatos activities as applied to things, with the instructor writing the activities on the board as they are suggested.

The same procedure is then followed with "nature," "other people," and "ourselves."

Response of the Pilot Group: Summary of Discussion

Toward Things

Eros	Thanatos
Inventing	Looting and vandalizing
Creating	Breaking
Making	Stealing
Building	Burning
Polishing	Wasting
Caring for and repairing	Neglecting
Cleaning and lubricating	
Collecting and classifying	
Studying assets and qualities	
Applying artistry and enhancing beauty	
Respecting function in usage	
Sharing and giving possessions	
Producing music	

Toward Nature and Animals

Cultivating useful or beautiful growing things	Picking wild flowers
Reforesting	Disfiguring landscape by littering
Observing sunrise and sunset	Causing forest fires
Hearing birds' songs	Chopping trees for firewood
Basking in the sun	Skinning birch bark
Riding horseback	Writing names in caves
Collecting rocks or shells	Breaking stalagmites
Feeding wild squirrels	Spoiling nature for others, either maliciously, carelessly, ignorantly or mockingly
Picnicking in the park	
Hunting or fishing within the limits of the law, according to a code of	Polluting water supplies
	Polluting air

ethics and the laws of nature
Raising animals
Training animals
Conserving animal life
Sponsoring the SPCA or endorsing its practices

Creating unsightly and unhealthful natural places
Letting plants and animals die from lack of care
Hunting illegally
Tying cans to dog's tails
Chunking rocks at toads
Pulling wings off butterflies
Using animals as amusement—cock fights
Running over turtles and terrapins with a car
Killing harmless snakes and armadillos
Teasing animals to make them vicious and then whipping them when they get vicious
Pouring kerosene on animals and setting fire to them to watch them suffer

Toward Other People

Eros

Serving as leader
Contributing time, money or effort to civic enterprises
Participating in politics
Serving as foster parent
Competing in sports
Driving cautiously
Listening
Being honest
Cultivating a sense of humor
Teaching skills and imparting knowledge to others

Thanatos

Behaving violently
Injuring others physically
Driving recklessly
Exploiting others
Driving while intoxicated
Violating others sexually
Using sleep as an escape
Ignoring or mistrusting others
Being apathetic or uninvolved
Throwing verbal bricks
Maligning reputations
Using sex as a weapon
Interfering with others' enjoyment of games and sports
Murdering

Toward Oneself

Fulfilling work responsibilities
Learning
Engaging in hobbies
Practicing skills
Expressing oneself creatively
Eating sensibly
Drinking moderately
Exercising regularly
Taking normal safety precautions
Being honest with oneself

Being adicted to alcohol, drugs, food
Mutilating self
Selecting dangerous hobbies without normal safety precautions: sky diving, scuba diving, hot rod racing, surfing
Engaging in destructive sexual practices
Failing to maintain physical vigor
Driving oneself unrealistically in work
Suicide

UNIT IV—PROMISING FOR THE FUTURE

SESSION 1—OVERCOMMITTERS AND UNDERCOMMITTERS

Better it is that thou shouldest not vow, than that thou shouldest vow and not pay.

Ecclesiastes, V:5

Organization

Regular classroom seating.

Equipment

Blue and gray tags of colored construction paper, 2 x 3 in.; transparent tape, paper and pencil for each group.

Instructions

"Some people commit themselves too easily and too frequently. Others seldom commit themselves, and when they do, it is done reluctantly. If you feel you are an overcommitter, put on a blue tag. If you are an undercommitter, put on a gray tag.

"Remember, blue tags are the people who make many promises to others and intend to fulfill these promises. The gray tags are those who are reluctant to promise. You must classify yourself one way or the other. In this exercise, there are only two categories.

"Now, form groups of five or six people, all with tags the same color. Some groups will be comprised of overcommitters. Other groups will be comprised of undercommitters."

Activity

Class participants form into groups according to the instructions.

Instructions

"In your groups, you will discuss how you each function in relation to promises or commitments. We want to determine

248

whether or not people with the same color tags have anything in common. Discuss also the ways you are different from people who have the other color tag and how you feel about them. Write your conclusions on the paper. Select one person to be the recorder for your group."

Activity

Discussions are conducted in the groups and the conclusions are recorded on the papers.

Instructions

"We will hear the report from each group in turn, beginning first with the overcommitters."

Activity

A report is heard from each overcommitter group.

Instructions

"What comments have you on the reports of the over-committers? Now, let us hear from the undercommitters."

Activity

A report is heard from each undercommitter group.

Instructions

"Are there any comments on the reports? How do overcommitters feel about undercommitters? How do undercommitters feel about overcommitters?"

Activity

Blue-tag groups give a report on their feelings about the gray-tag groups, and vice versa.

Instructions

"Now discuss in your groups what you would consider to be an optimum level of commitment. Just exactly how much, when and how should a person commit himself? When and under what circumstances should we make promises to others?

Activity

Group members discuss the question of the optimum level of commitment.

Instructions

"From the papers of each group, I will make a composite report which will describe the behavior and feelings of the blue tag people and the gray tag people. I will post your findings on the bulletin board tomorrow, and we can discuss them in the next class if you wish to make further comments."

Response of the Pilot Group: Collation

The aims of the undercommitters and the overcommitters are the same. They both want to keep from losing friends.

Both do what they do because they are unsure of what they want, and neither want to be told they are wrong.

Both are impulsive and need to learn to weigh situations.

Response of Overcommitters

I am an overcommitter. Out of a sense of duty and as a result of guilt, I commit myself to obligations I do not want. I promise more than I should expect of myself.

In a moment of overconfident enthusiasm and blind impulse, I readily commit myself without assessing the situation. I do not define the limits of the situation, my capabilities, and my time.

I spread myself too thin and find I can't carry through. Because I am afraid of failing if I do just one thing, I push myself to do so many things that I am bound to fail at some of them. I do not want to choose.

I am afraid of being alone. I am eager to please. I want recognition and to feel important, needed and accepted by others. I cannot say "no" for fear of being rejected and losing friendship.

I trust people to have the same values I have and, as things turn out, they don't.

I am competitive with other overcommitters and have friction with them.

When I overcommit, I am disgusted with myself. I am angry at myself for being controlled and at the other party for pushing me around.

Response of Undercommitters

I am an undercommitter. I am reluctant to commit myself unless I am absolutely sure I can fulfill the commitment. I always fulfill the contracts I make, but I rarely make any.

I fear getting into something I can't handle, so I like to leave a loophole to get out of my commitment.

I am not a person who volunteers. I am afraid of choice, responsibility, and failure. Undercommitment gives me a feeling of being safe.

I distrust myself. I distrust others. Since I am afraid I will fail other people, I am basically passive and depend on others to make the choices.

I avoid conflict, argument, and rejection by trying to please and being quiet. I agree by saying, "Yes, you're right." Sometimes I am dishonest when I don't want to do something.

Most of the time I tell myself that I really enjoy being independent, that I choose to remain uninvolved with others, that I really don't care. I tell myself I do not need to earn or buy friendship because I don't need friends. Really, I am afraid of being alone.

I feel angry with myself for being walked on and pushed around. I feel insecure, apathetic, lazy and indecisive.

How Overcommitters Feel about Undercommitters

I would not like to be as passive as undercommitters are. I always have something to do, and there is a certain amount of satisfaction in accepting responsibility. I would like to enjoy a little peace and quiet without pressure, as they do. I would like to not have so many demands on me.

How Undercommitters Feel about Overcommitters

I see no advantage in being an overcommitter. They would rather do an unpleasant job than ask for help from someone else. They are incapable of saying "no" if the asker is persistent.

An overcommitter complains about the extra load he takes on. This is done for prestige, but it usually backfires because the load will be too great and he can't accomplish it. In the final analysis, the undercommitter will be on top because he can complete his contract and the overcommitter will not be able to complete his.

Overcommitters are extremely impulsive and can be walked on.

I would rather be dead than be an overcommitter—but I die anyway in the end, because I never get a chance to join in the activity or get close to anyone.

What Is an Optimum Level of Commitment?

An optimum level of commitment is achieved when . . .

A person knows himself and where he places his values.

He makes commitments related to his own values rather than someone else's.

He relates his commitments realistically to his abilities to follow through.

He takes time to evaluate the consequences of the commitment before he makes it.

He makes commitments which produce a minimum anger level toward himself and toward others.

If a person can make commitments which are advantageous to himself and others, he enjoys a feeling of self-confidence, a sense of accomplishment, a satisfaction with his own level of responsibility. He maintains satisfying relationships with others.

SESSION 2—LEARNING TO SAY "NO" TO PART AND "YES" TO PART

Organization
Circle or amphitheater formation.

Equipment
None.

Instructions
"Part of learning to make a realistic commitment is to assess what the person is offering and to realize that it is usually not necessary to accept or reject the offer as one complete package. It is possible to accept part of an offer and reject another part. It is possible to set limits or conditions on the acceptance. Numerous factors may be delimited: time, effort, equipment, weather, etc.

"In the exercise today, one person will make a request or an offer to another person. The second person is to answer, accepting one portion of the offer or request and rejecting a portion. The first person may either request or offer help or information, instruction, entertainment, money, etc. No matter what is offered or requested, the second person is to accept only part of what is offered or give only part of what he is asked to give.

"Are there any questions? If not, who would like to start the exercise?"

Activity
A volunteer initiates the activity, choosing a second person to whom he makes his request or offer. If someone has difficulty in accepting part or rejecting part, the instructor may assist as necessary or request assistance from the group. When a person is successful in dividing the offer or request, he then takes his turn in making an offer to someone else. When a person fails to both accept and reject, that is, he takes all of what is offered or agrees to do all that he is asked to do, he loses his turn to make an offer or request of someone else.

Note: Through a simple, game-like exercise, the participant examines the nature of commitment.

SESSION 3—LEARNING TO POSTPONE TO A DEFINITE TIME

Organization
Circle or amphitheater formation.

Equipment
None.

Instructions
"Part of learning to make a realistic commitment relates to learning to postpone a commitment. However, it is not enough to tell the other person that you cannot answer him now: the device of postponing *indefinitely* is a roundabout method of refusing the offer. You must learn to say, 'I can not answer right now, but I will tell you at/on (*specific time*).'

"In today's exercise, one person will make an offer to a person he selects. The second person is to answer by postponing his acceptance to a definite time. The first person can either accept the postponement or say that it will not be possible for him to wait that long for an answer. In the latter case, the negotiation may continue until the two people reach an agreement as to the time of the definitive postponement.

"Are there any questions? If not, who would like to start the exercise?"

Activity
Someone volunteers to begin the activity, and the participants follow the directions. If anyone has difficulty in postponing, the instructor may assist as necessary. Each person who postpones successfully is allowed to make an offer to someone else. If a person fails to postpone successfully, he loses his turn to make an offer, and the first person selects another recipient for his inquiry.

NOTE: In another game-like exercise, the participant asserts himself through postponing his commitment.

SESSION 4—LEARNING TO GIVE THE PARTIAL ANSWER

Theoretical Presentation

To avoid hasty and impulsive commitments, it is desirable to learn to give the partial answer. This type of answer avoids the pitfall of overcommitment, in which case the person is likely to become angry because he has promised to do more than he really feels like doing. The postponement, which is tied in with the partial answer, gives the person time to consult with others and to collect knowledge and information on which to base his commitment, as well as to examine his feelings to determine areas of vulnerability. He can also anticipate various eventualities and consider the emotional dimensions of each solution.

In this lesson we will practice responding to a request by giving a partial answer. Part of what is asked is to be accepted, part is to be rejected, and part is to be postponed. Of that part which is postponed, part is to be accepted and part rejected. Acceptances and rejections may be conditional. Postponement, however, cannot be vague or indefinite.

Remember, we are defining a partial answer to include four processes:

Step 1: Certain parts of the request you will turn down.
Step 2: Certain parts of the request you will accept.
Step 3: Certain parts of the request you will hold in abeyance, postponing to a definite time.
Step 4: When the definite time arrives, you will turn down part of what remained undecided and accept part of what remained undecided.

The answer may be limited or postponed on the basis of any one of several factors: knowledge, time, amount of activity, quality of performance expected, equipment available, etc.

The following interchange will illustrate the four steps.

Mary: "I would like to go to the movies tonight. Would you?" (Request)

Betty: "I would like to go to the movies (Step 2). I cannot go tonight as my husband and I have already made plans to go to the Club, where we are expected to attend a meeting (Step 1). Could we go some other night this week or next? (Step 3)"

Mary: "I could go any night except Friday."

Betty: "Let me check with my husband to see what his plans are and when I can have the car. I'll call you back after lunch (Step 3)." (After lunch Betty calls back.) "I checked with Joe. He says he has to work tomorrow night anyway and doesn't mind staying home with the kids as long as I am back by 11:00 P.M. I can have the car. Could we go tomorrow night?"

Mary: "That would be fine with me."

Betty: "What picture did you want to see? Did you have a special one in mind?"

Mary: "I wanted to see *Love is Forever*."

Betty: "That's great with me. I like those mushy ones (Step 4, Acceptance). I'd rather go out to North Park if it is playing there. I don't like to drive downtown at night. (Step 4, Rejection) I'll pick you up around seven tomorrow night."

Mary: "Good. I'll be ready."

"That interchange will give you some idea of what I mean by the four steps of the partial answer. Now let us try it."

Organization

Circle or amphitheater formation.

Equipment

None.

Instructions

"I will write the four processes on the board.

"Who would like to start? The volunteer will have the option of selecting someone whom he will ask for a commitment. This person is to respond with a partial answer, including all four steps. If he manages to give the partial answer successfully, he can then ask for a commitment from someone else. The class will decide whether or not he has been successful in giving his partial answer."

Activity

The volunteer asks the person of his selection to make a commitment as to what he is willing to do. The class determines whether or not the answer is acceptable as a partial commitment.

If so, the answerer becomes the asker, selects another person and poses a question.

The procedure continues for most of the period. About ten minutes before the close of the class, the leader asks for comments on experiences with the partial answer.

SESSION 5—THE PROMISE[1]

Theoretical Presentation

The problem of commitments and how to handle them is and always has been an integral part of common life—so much so that it is one of the main concerns of the law itself. Even before men could write, the older members of each group passed on their laws and customs to the succeeding generations. Wherever men have lived together, they have found it necessary to develop rules of conduct to make possible their living together amicably. Many of the codes of behavior, which ultimately became law, concern the responsibility involved when one person makes a promise to another.

A promise is one person's pledge to another to do or not do a thing specified. This declaration gives the recipient a right to expect performance or forbearance of a specified act. A promise provides the other person with grounds for hope or expectation.

The lightness with which many of us approach promises is illustrated by the anecdote in which the boy telephones his girl friend, "I'd cross the highest mountain, I'd ford the widest river, I'd sail the roughest sea, I'd walk through the hottest desert and crawl through fire and brimstone to be with you. Well, I'll see you tonight if it doesn't rain."

Many of the problems that arise in interpersonal relationships concern the obligations we owe when we promise and what we have a right to expect from a person when he makes a promise to us.

Some of us promise too easily and therefore we are unable to carry out our promises. Some of us are so reluctant to promise that we avoid opportunities for satisfying mutuality. Some persons take frivolous promises seriously; others take solemn promises

---

NOTE: This lecture examines principles related to promises, thus seeking to understand those principles which have been written into the law. This approach manifests the consensual validity inherent in the human experience of promising.

[1] Principles for this session were taken from Kling, Samuel G.: *Your Legal Advisor*. New York, Permabooks, 1955, and Ross, Martin J.: *Handbook of Everyday Law*. New York, Harper, 1959.

lightly. Some people make promises they have no intention of keeping, while others keep promises they have really never made.

The consequences which result from these situations are, at the very least, annoying, upsetting and bewildering. At worst, they are catastrophically tragic.

The ability to promise is a requisite of maturity. Promising involves not only the ability to make promises which are comfortably within the limits of one's capabilities but also the ability to carry out all the promises one is willing to make. Promising involves numerous concommitants of emotional maturity: awareness, solemnity, voluntary initiative and mutuality.

The concept of maturity as a necessity for contract-making has been written into our legal structure through many types of contracts. Some, for example, cannot be made legally by a person under 21 years of age. If such a contract is made, it is not an enforceable contract.

A person of unsound mind is presumed to have insufficient grasp on reality to make a contract. Here again we find the concept of maturity embodied in the law: an accurate grasp of reality is a function of psychological maturity.

Since the ability to promise is presumptive of maturity, the mature person should be wary of negotiating contracts with those who do not have the psychological maturity to carry out a promise involving future behavior. It is pertinent to inquire into the competency of the promiser as well as into the terms of the contract.

A legal contract formalizes, usually in writing, a strong and solemn binding promise between people. Let us consider some of the legal principles and elements involved in making contracts and legally binding promises. Let us see what the law stipulates regarding conditions and responsibilities of promising. Perhaps legal codes can help us in arriving at responsibility in the simple, nonlegal situations of everyday life.

The Contract Itself

Awareness is a prerequisite to a promise. Both parties must be aware that they are entering into a contract. Their words and actions must reveal a serious intention to create a contract. Both sides must indicate a mutual intention to be bound and obligated, giving something in exchange for something else. Even though it be something as unsubstantial as a peppercorn, each party must have contributed something toward the creation of the contract.

An offer which consists of a request to do something immoral or unlawful is, at the outset, a violation of the principles of contract making. The topic, purpose, or subject matter of the contract must not be in violation of any law or contrary to the public policy or morals of the place where the contract is made or to be performed.

A contract, whether written or verbal, is presumed to contain all the provisions agreed upon. There can be no hidden provisions and there should be no requirements buried in ambiguities. Fraud, deceit, misrepresentation, or coercion in the making of an agreement can invalidate the agreement or make it voidable at the option of the person deceived or coerced.

Basically, a contract consists of an offer by one party and an acceptance by the other party. Basic principles govern both the offer and the acceptance.

The Offer

An offer is a promise which is conditional upon its being accepted. When the offer is made, it is presumed that the person making the offer is willing to do what he is offering. The person making an offer has the right to direct his offer to a specific person. Only the person to whom it is directed has the right to accept.

An offer made to anyone in a group of people gives anyone in that group the right to accept it. A person making a general offer must accept anyone who is willing to accept the offer on his terms. Once the offer is accepted, the offer is thereby closed to others in the group, unless the person making the offer elects otherwise.

An offer with a time limit may be withdrawn before the end of the time period unless action has been taken to bind the offerer to keep the offer in force for the entire time period.

If an offer specifies the time within which it must be accepted, the offer is considered to have lapsed if it is not accepted or extended within that time. If no time is specified, but if the offer is not accepted within a reasonable time, it will be considered to have lapsed automatically. What constitutes a *reasonable* time depends upon the particular facts and circumstances involved.

The Acceptance

Only an accepted offer ripens into a contract. The acceptance may consist of a reciprocal promise or an act specified by the terms of the offer.

Any change in the terms of the offer by the person to whom it is made is a rejection of the offer originally made. A change creates a counteroffer, which becomes a contract only if it is subsequently accepted by the person who made the original offer.

If the acceptor unilaterally attempts to change—or changes— the provisions of the contract after he has accepted the contract, the contract is breached, and he can be held for violation of the contract.

An effort to accept the offer after it has expired is only a counteroffer and ripens into a contract only if it is accepted by the person who made the original offer.

An offer which is not accepted does not give any right to the person to whom it is made. The offer terminates with its rejection by the person to whom it is made, and ordinarily it cannot be revived by him subsequently.

Legal practice has endeavored to establish the responsibilities of one human being toward another in their mutual actions. If a person fails to fulfill these responsibilities, he may be required to pay money damages or to provide other appropriate kinds of relief or remedies in order to make up for his failure to fulfill his responsibilities.

Summary and Conclusion

The foregoing practical, reasonable elements and principles of contract law should be absorbed and considered in making promises and accepting promises in everyday life. Before making a commitment, a person should carefully consider the subject matter and details of the commitment, his ability to carry it out, his real wants and desires, and the situation and abilities of the other person involved.

Breaking a commitment causes damage in personal relations as well as in legal relations. Failure to fulfill responsibilities results in other types of damage in personal relationships: anger, disappointment, rejection, annoyance, rage, and frustration.

If interpersonal relationships are to be furthered, commitments must be fulfilled. They should be made carefully and thoughtfully, and once made, they should be kept.

SESSION 6—RECOGNIZING PROBLEMS IN THE PROMISE SITUATION

Organization

Participants are seated in a large circle, double circle, triple circle, or amphitheater style.

Equipment

Paired slips of paper, with two slips bearing the same number, one marked "offer" and the other marked "acceptance." Each slip gives instructions as to what is to be done.

Instructions

"Your paper will state whether you are to make the offer or make the acceptance. The paper will state the type of problem to which you are to respond. Each situation presented is a clear violation of one of the principles of the contractual situation, as previously outlined.

"The problem will be for you to devise the circumstances and subject matter of the offer and acceptance. If on your slip you find some specific distortion of the contractual situation, you should try to incorporate this distortion into the circumstances and subject matter which you devise.

"Either party may be violating one of the contractual principles we have studied. If a distortion or violation is suggested on your slip, imagine a role for yourself, and elaborate the situation as you choose. Try to disguise the violation subtly, so that it is not readily apparent to the person making the acceptance. Attempt to be exploitative in regard to the rights of the other person. Take away his rights and privileges if you can do so.

"If you have no violation on your slip, your first effort will be devoted to discovering what is wrong with the other person's offer or acceptance. Do your best to uphold your rights and privileges in the situation. Get as much as you can and give as little as possible.

NOTE: This session attempts to isolate and demonstrate the principles outlined in the previous lecture. Though complex and difficult, the exercise makes interesting points.

"Both of you may invent situations, but you must stay clearly within bounds of the problem given you."

Activity

The following slips are passed out. Each situation is presented before the group in turn by number, starting with the offer and following with the acceptance. Various kinds of special conditions may be brought in by the two parties as appropriate. In each situation the group is asked to evaluate both the offer and the acceptance according to the principles outlined in the previous chapter.

Offer #1. Ask a person to promise something which is illegal or against the rules of the institution.

Acceptance #1. Do not accept the offer if it involves doing something which is unlawful or contrary to the public policy or morals of the place where the contract is made or to be performed.

Offer #2. Direct an offer to the group and then deny the offer to the person who accepts it.

Acceptance #2. Accept the offer which is offered to the group. When the offerer denies the offer to you, insist on your right to have the offer carried out, since it was an open offer to anyone in the group.

Offer #3. Make a valid and legitimate offer.

Acceptance #3. In accepting the offer, change the terms, preferably to something which will be very good for you, but which you know the offerer won't like.

Offer #4. Offer something you are not willing to do, then withdraw it after the other person has accepted the offer and agreed to do his part.

Acceptance #4. Accept the offer and agree to do your part in the contract. When the offer is withdrawn, insist that the other person carry out the contract, since he made the agreement.

Offer #5. Make an offer. The other person will reject the offer, then change his mind and try to accept it. Insist that the offer no longer holds once it has been rejected.

Acceptance #5. Reject the offer. After you have rejected it, decide you will accept it.

Offer #6. Try to extract a promise that has an indefinite or unreasonably long time limit.

Acceptance #6. Promise only after reasonable time limits have been set by discussion between the two parties.

Offer #7. Try to get the other person to promise by threatening him.

Acceptance #7. Make a promise while threatened. After having made it, insist that even if you did promise while being threatened, you are not under any obligation to keep the forced promise.

Offer #8. Make a serious offer. When the person accepts in jest or humor, attempt to enforce the agreement as if it were a true contract.

Acceptance #8. Accept the offer in jest or with humor in an attempt to avoid a serious commitment.

Offer #9. Make an unrealistic offer in jest or humor. After the person accepts it seriously, attempt to avoid it as an offer made in jest.

Acceptance #9. Accept the offer seriously and tell the person you are counting on his carrying it out.

Offer #10. In making an agreement with the other person, misrepresent some fact in order to get the other person to enter into the agreement. After the agreement is made, slyly let him know that the misrepresented fact was not true and try to persuade him to go ahead and fulfill the agreement anyway.

Acceptance #10. Enter into the agreement with the other person because of what he says to you. When you are later informed of a misrepresentation that moved you to make the agreement, tell the other person that the misrepresentation makes the contract void. Stick by this and tell him off!

Offer #11. Make an agreement with the other person. After the agreement is made, bring out a number of hidden conditions which were not part of the agreement and insist that they be included in the agreement.

Acceptance #11. After the agreement is made, when hidden conditions are brought up, insist that they are not part of the original agreement and that you have no obligation to fulfill them.

Offer #12. Take some kind of action similar to that which would be taken in making a contract. The other person will not object to the action you take at the time you take it. Insist that he has made a contract, even though he was not aware that a contract was being offered at the time the action was taken.

Acceptance #12. Deny that you made a contract when you did not object to the action that was being taken. Regardless of how forceful the other person is, insist that you did not make a contract.

SESSION 7—SIGNING THE COMMITMENT CONTRACT

Prior Preparation Required

(Presented at the close of the preceding period.)

"For the next time, will you please bring to class some personal item which is worth between two and five dollars. (The amount may vary with the situation. It should be substantial enough to lend some significance and dignity to the transaction of the contractual agreement.) We are going to place these personal belongings in escrow, to be held by the instructor until completion of our next activity concerning promise and commitment. You are likely familiar with the term "escrow." It is sometimes called "earnest money." When you are buying a house and you submit a contract of purchase, you include with the purchase contract a certain amount of money to indicate your good faith in making the offer. If you fail to follow through on your contractual obligations, whereas the seller follows through on his obligations, you forfeit the money you placed in escrow.

"So remember that you are to bring to class next time an escrow item of personal belongings worth between two and five dollars. If you fail to bring an escrow item, you will not be able to participate in the experiment."

Theoretical Presentation

Most of the promises which people make to each other are never written, yet we continuously make promises of one kind or another and in hundreds of different ways.

In personal relationships, the responsibility of making and then keeping promises should be taken as seriously as if there were money involved and a legal contract required. When promises are made only to be broken, the result is anger, disappointment, hurt, or separation, any of which severely damage the relationships they do not wholly destroy.

Organization

Regular classroom arrangement.

Equipment

Mimeographed copies of the Commitment Contract, pencils, a box in which escrow items may be collected, 3 in. brown gummed tape for sealing the escrow box, paper.

Instructions

"Today we are going to experiment with a written contract. An actual legal contract has been adapted to our particular situation. We are going to use a written legal-type contract for a nonlegal situation."

"Only those of you who brought escrow items may participate today. The others will sit on the sidelines and observe. An individual escrow item is essential equipment for today's class.

"In large letters on a sheet of paper, print information regarding an offer you are willing to make to anyone in the class. This offer should be a promise to perform some service for another person. The person who makes the offer will be called the Offerer.

"Move about the room, reading offers of others and showing your own. If you find someone whose offer you wish to accept, or if someone wishes to accept your offer, pair with that person. Each person should end up with a partner. The one who accepts the offer will be called the Offeree.

"Each of you will state to the other what you are willing to do. Discuss your commitments to each other and then agree on what each of you is willing to commit himself to do.

"When you have negotiated and reached agreement, each of you will fill in the written contract and sign it. Leave your contract with me, and place your escrow items in the box here. Be sure your escrow item is marked with your name.

"At the next class, we will see if the contracts have been fulfilled by either or both persons.

"If both persons have fulfilled their commitments, each one will repossess the item he placed in escrow.

"If the Offerer has fulfilled his commitment and the Offeree has failed to fulfill his commitment, the Offerer will repossess the item he put up and will also receive the Offeree's escrow

item as *damages* due him because of the Offeree's failure to fulfill
his commitment.

"The reverse of the above will result, of course, if the Offerer
fails to fulfill and the Offeree does fulfill.

"If neither person fulfills, then each will receive the item
put up by the other.

"However, if the circumstances are such that one person has
stood ready and able to fulfill, but failed to do so or was prevented
from doing so because of the failure of the other person to
fulfill or because of the action of the other person, the one who
was ready and able will regain his own item as well as the item
of the other person.

"Is there anyone who does not understand what we are going
to do?" (The leader may need to repeat parts of the explanation.)

Activity

Participants select partners, negotiate one of the written
contracts, and sign it. During the activity, the instructor answers
any questions concerning the procedure. He refuses to answer
questions concerning the content of any commitment.

After signing the contract form, the pairs deposit their escrow
items in the escrow box. At the end of the period, the escrow
box is sealed.

The signed contracts are collected and both the escrow box
and the contracts are kept until the following class period, when
the parties will appear in court.

COMMITMENT CONTRACT

I, ..., The Offerer, hereby offer unto
............................., the Offeree, the following:

....
....
....

I, the Offerer, hereby deposit in escrow with the Class Instructor the following item of property: ....
to be held in escrow and disposed of pursuant to applicable rules of law.

The Offeree, by signing his name hereto, hereby accepts the offer made by the Offerer, and Offeree agrees to the following obligation on his part:

....
....
....

The Offeree hereby deposits in escrow with the Class Instructor the following item of property: ....
to be held in escrow and disposed of pursuant to applicable rules of law.

In the event of a difference of opinion between the parties on any question or subject relating to this Commitment Contract, the decision of a jury appointed by the Class shall be final and binding on both parties. Disposition of the items placed in escrow shall be made by said Jury.

Witness our hands this .... day of ....,
19......, at the City of................, County of................
State of....................

....
Offerer

....
Offeree

SESSION 8—COURTROOM APPEARANCE

Organization

A portion of the room is set aside as the Jury Box, in which the jury will be seated.

Equipment

The sealed box full of the escrow items from the last period, the sheaf of signed Commitment Contracts.

Instructions

"Our first duty today is to select members of the jury from those who were present at the last session. We will need five for the jury. When his own case comes before the court, a juror will step down and be replaced by another person."

Activity

The jury is selected and seated in the jury box. The jurors elect their foreman, who will preside over the jury's deliberations after presentation of all the evidence and testimony on the case at hand.

Instructions

"The jury will have in hand copies of the contracts and will call each case before the court, in turn.

"As called, each pair will appear before the Court. Each person will testify as to the facts, what each person did or failed to do in regard to fulfillment of the contract.

"If the jury finds that the contract has been properly fulfilled, the escrow items will be returned to each party. If the contract has not been fulfilled by one party and has been by the other, the aggrieved party will be awarded his own item and the escrow item of the other party.

"If neither party fulfilled, each will receive the item put in escrow by the other party.

"If one party failed to fulfill and the other party was ready and able to fulfill but did not do so or was prevented from doing so because of the failure of the other person, that person, then, who was ready and able, will receive his own item and that of the other person.

"Any situation not covered by the rules stated above will be resolved by decisions of the jurors on the basis of their sense of justice and fairness."

Activity

Each pair in turn appears before the Court. The jurors (including the foreman) discuss and deliberate upon the evidence and instructions, then make their decisions and state them to the foreman. The foreman announces the decision (verdict), and the escrow items are awarded by the foreman, all in accordance with the verdict of the majority of the jurors.

When all the pairs have finished presenting their cases in court, the class may be dismissed, or a discussion may be held regarding the problems encountered.

EPILOGUE

My PARENTS TOLD ME:
Children should be seen and not heard.
Do not talk back.
Do not display feelings.
It is better to keep your problems to yourself.
A happy face will get you through a tough situation.
Turn the other cheek.
It is not proper to get angry.
Uncontrolled anger is a sign of weakness.
If you get angry, people will not like you.

Once
I was afraid of responsibility. I exaggerated responsibility.
I shifted responsibility to others or permitted others to take mine.
I was overly dependent, and drove people away by letting them control me until they were tired of it.
I made snap decisions.
I attempted too many things and never completed any.
I had a contempt for knowledge and new experience.
I reached a point when I thought I knew it all, and I quit growing.
I isolated myself and resisted communication.
I shared only small talk. Sometimes I talked with no meaning.
I tried to stifle my feelings.
I was imperturbable.
I tried to show I was above problems.
I contained my feelings by finding fault, excusing, forgiving.
I was paralyzed into inaction for fear of being hurt.
Negative feelings overwhelmed positive feelings.

NOTE: The epilogue is a collation from a number of sessions, framed into one statement. In their own words, the participants in the pilot group tell of their search for the kind of self-change the sessions were designed to produce.

Sometimes I even had a wish to fail. I did not want to succeed because success could be uncomfortable.

Sometimes I just stayed in bed, worrying about a problem instead of trying to do something about it.

I felt tired, heavy, and chained.

I missed a lot of living.

I felt hopeless.

I felt helpless.

Stifled, my feelings destroyed me as a human being.

Then

I began to feel what a sham I was.

What a childish front for adult love!

I asked

How can I overcome the need to blot out the painful past and evade the fearful future?

Do I really believe that an old dog can learn new tricks?

I have to get at the root of why I have failed.

I have to understand why I have allowed myself to be destroyed.

But

To acquire the skills necessary for survival takes push and drive, and I have little.

Sometimes confronting life with zest and push is a bothersome effort.

Gradually

I have begun to feel new insights.

I have found out I am not unique or different.

No man is an island. I need other people to fulfill my needs.

All of us are mature in some ways and immature in others.

Instead of thinking I can't do anything at all, I will acquire knowledge of my assets and limitations.

When I don't know, I will discover.

Instead of latching on to things at random, I will set goals— realistic ones for a change.

I may not have the same problems and interests as others, but if I open up, they will open up too. Then we can share ourselves.

Now I realize

I have life space. It contains all aspects of me: my body, my health, my sexual relationships, my perception, my introspections, my sharing and communication, my past and my future.

It contains my self-protection, my self-assertion, my self-modification, my flexibility.

My responsibility for my life space produces my self-esteem, my identity, my wholeness.

Now I affirm

I will jump into the mainstream of life.

I will admit to myself that my feelings of insecurity are there, but most of the time I will hide them from others.

Instead of making myself look more important or less important than I really am, I will keep myself in perspective.

I will not rely on others to speak, think, fight, and feel for me.

I will allow my dry tears to be real ones.

I will exhibit openly instead of inhibiting inwardly.

I will stop using language as a cloak.

I will try to turn myself inside out. To those I trust, I will talk and tell.

I will try to understand what others verbalize, sensing their needs and interests, and empathizing by seeing their point of view.

Instead of thinking I need no help, I will sometimes seek help.

I will distinguish between times when I should and when I should not seek help in problem solving.

I will recognize and assert a certain amount of independence and avoid holding on to dependency when it is inappropriate and destructive.

I will submit to peer review and function as part of a team.

I will seek relationships wherein individuals contribute to each other.

I will follow through with action.

The infinite space of affirmation still creates an awful fear.

BOOK II
PHILOSOPHY AND METHODOLOGY

BASIC PHILOSOPHICAL PRINCIPLES

Interpersonal Communication with Intimate Peers Is a
Core Experience in the Process of Living

COMMUNICATION UTILIZES THAT one talent which most clearly distinguishes man from other animals: language. Only human beings have the ability to express nuances of thought and feeling through words. Most of what we call human characteristics are expressed and developed through meaningful noises directed toward other human beings and through meaningful marks to be interpreted by other men.

Through expression of feelings we become related and remain related to others. Through expression we give clues which offer others the opportunity to meet our needs and enjoy, as a consequence of so doing, the pleasurable experience of acting unselfishly.

The expressive person provides sanction of expressiveness in others. One who fails to express his own feelings constricts us in the expression of ours. Only when others express their feelings are we then offered the opportunity to act in such a way as to meet their needs and enjoy the experience of acting unselfishly.

Accurate, clear, honest, mutually affirmative communication with others produces reliable attachments and satisfying fellowship. Such communication enables us to have our individuality acknowledged, accepted, and even honored. The person who learns expressiveness becomes able to relate to others without the need to exploit or dominate, or the need to be submissive and dependent. He is free to leave others free.

In most instances, man becomes aware of communication only when it breaks down. When our communicative processes are impaired, we cannot share the basic experience of commonality with others or feel the gratifying satisfactions of love from those significant to us. We find it virtually impossible to ask for what we need—whether it be information, direction, cooperation, communion, expressiveness, empathy, or reassurance.

Communication that is clumsy, confused, or insensitive breeds isolation, fear, suspiciousness, helplessness, hostility, disinterest, malice, prejudice, and self-pity. Inadequate communication breeds erroneous ideas and concepts. Furthermore, the resulting social alienation leads to the construction of protective walls around the self to avoid further hurt and rejection. Such barricades produce additional disturbance and distortion of the communicative processes. At some point, a crisis is precipitated, and the person is classified as mentally ill.

Jurgen Ruesch has described communication as the "social matrix of psychiatry," and attributes mental illness to a disturbed communicative process.[1]

Communicative Effort Is a Responsibility Inherent in Adulthood

It is presumed that the adult has the responsibility to communicate his wants, needs, ideas, opinions, and feelings to others. One who desires to be understood by others must provide sufficient data for that understanding. It is also axiomatic that he has the responsibility to respond to the communications of others— to seek understanding of their needs and to participate in meeting these needs.

The person who expects others to understand him, though he has supplied no data, can be aptly compared to the infant who emits enigmatic noises that are essentially unidentifiable, but which stimulate adults to make a series of guesses as to the nature of his problem. Is he wet? Is he hungry? Does he hurt? If so, where? Is he lonely or frightened? Does he merely want attention?

In dealing with a child, the parent, as an adult, has the responsibility to understand the helpless infant's cry and to meet his needs through a trial-and-error process. By eliminating the causes one by one, the parent arrives at some diagnosis of the

---

[1] Ruesch, Jurgen, and Bateson, Gregory: *Communication, the Social Matrix of Psychiatry.* New York, Norton, 1951.

infant's problem and proceeds to take some kind of action. If the infant stops crying, the parent's diagnosis is validated. If the crying continues, the adult must haphazardly continue his efforts until one or another method solves the problem.

As the child learns to talk, he is expected to make his communications more and more specific and gradually eliminate the need for guesswork and deduction on the part of others. A person who has achieved maturity has accepted the responsibility for communicating his own ideas and feelings, and he no longer expects others to be able to understand his needs unless he makes them known.

Catharsis Is One of the Major Functions of Communication

Actually, one of the foremost reasons or justifications for expression is the catharsis or purification which results from it. Unexpressed emotions cause intrapsychic problems. Expressed words become substitutes for physical aggressiveness and destructiveness toward others and toward the self. Pent-up emotions, when expressed, are discharged, thus providing purgation and relief from disturbing symptoms. Expressed, emotions have a tendency to dissipate, even though the external situation has not changed and the behavior of others has not altered.

Paradoxically, the catharsis achieved by expression of negative and painful emotions makes possible the expression of positive and pleasurable feelings. In other words, expression of negative feelings leads ultimately to a positive liberating experience which produces happiness and contributes to mental health.

Communication Increases Self-Awareness and Helps an Individual to Achieve Self-Understanding

Communication enables a person to become aware of himself. His manifestation of his emotions through talking, facilitates his viewing of them. In fact, only when he expresses his emotions is this significant part of himself made fully available for his examination.

Communication of feelings helps one make the painful journey to the root of a problem. Contemplating and studying emotions, as well as the expression of emotions, makes it possible to recognize the differences between feelings, to experience discrete emotions and awareness of discrete sources. Expression charms away the complexities of problems, thus freeing the person from the restrictions imposed by past experience and enabling him to fully experience the present.

On the contrary, unexpressed emotions are unrecognizable except in an undifferentiated form labeled "nervousness" or "anxiety." Such dispersed and obscured feelings can only lead to further frustration, confusion, and depression.

Communication of Feelings Leads Frequently to Alteration of One's Own Actions but Less Frequently to Altering the Actions of Others

The person who knowledgeably examines his own feelings and actions can increase his ability at self-correction. When he becomes aware of the fact that his previous responses have been in error, he can learn to anticipate events and to modify his subsequent reactions and actions.

It must be emphasized that the purpose of expression of feelings is not to alter someone else's action; the other person may or may not choose to alter his action as a result of the communication. Such remarks as "I told him how I felt about his behavior and he hasn't changed a bit" indicate a total lack of understanding of the purpose of expressing feelings.

Self-Confidence and Self-Esteem Are Concommitants of Participation in the Processes of Living

"I only wish I had some self-confidence" is a familiar threnody. The idle wish implies belief in a magic or ritual practice which, once discovered, could produce the happy result. The basic misconception is that what is lacking is confidence. The emphasis placed on the word *confidence* implies that all would be well if the individual could only develop confidence in a self that already exists and is psychologically fit.

Indeed, it is not self-confidence which is lacking. A truer statement would be, "I wish I had a self."

A person who lacks self-confidence has no defined self about which to be confident. His life is a drama performed by other actors. He relies on restraint from without rather than restraint from within. He acts capriciously and is unpredictable to himself as well as to others. When brought face to face with responsibility for his own actions, he asserts that choice and control lie within the spheres of responsibilities of others but not within his own realm. He is unable to behave in a way which will truly meet his own needs and promote his own growth and happiness. Lacking clear contact with a defined self, he is unable to experience self-confidence or true self-love.

Attaining self-confidence is a process. Learning to communicate is a process. Achieving interpersonal relatedness is a process. Getting well is a process.

Failure to recognize living as a process results in efforts to avoid participation in the mainstream of living and to disavow the need for self-change. Such restrictions lead inevitably to maladjustment and psychic pain.

On the contrary, understanding the significance of process can be a liberating experience. The dynamically oriented person discovers that error provides the opportunity for self-correction and the promise of further advance and growth.

Constructive participation in one's own life processes is the genesis of self-confidence. Confidence is the effect caused by self-directed effort.

The problem solving exercises of the Communication Class, with their emphasis on the processes involved and not on the end result, become a means toward the experience of self-confidence.

Chapter II

GENERAL METHODS

The Technique Is a Method-Oriented Technique and Not a Relationship Technique

T HE EXPERIMENTAL TECHNIQUE involves group study and inquiry into the nature of communicative relationships, with such relationships to be established elsewhere, outside the class. In contrast with individual and group psychotherapy, no attempt is made to foster relationships in the class meeting; members of the group and the instructor serve only as prototypes of other relationships. No attempt is made to develop relationships between instructor and class members, nor is any attempt made to have class members relate to each other in any specific or definitive manner. Most of the exercises are planned for a random selection of partners or groups.

The Use of the Paradox Is a Basic Teaching Device

Throughout the sessions, the conflictive and dynamic aspects of experience are presented through paradoxes. The outstanding value of the paradox is its ability to shock the participant into attention. Although two poles of a topic are often presented at the beginning of a lesson, the results of the exercise always demonstrate the inadequacy of such a two-value system. For instance, if the lesson deals with "positive and negative emotions," the conclusions reached in the discussion will be that all emotions have both positive and negative aspects. The simultaneous existence of opposite feelings within a person may cause inner conflict if the person is unable to tolerate these opposite feelings and to commit himself to action involving only *one* of the two feelings.

The abstract concepts related to the paradoxes of self-change are indeed difficult. Why is it necessary to become more angry in order to become less angry? Why must one become more self-concerned in order to become more selfless?

The technique has been to present problems without presenting solutions; to ask questions without providing answers—in fact, to often pose questions that are unanswerable; to present material applicable to personal experience without making intimate applications in the group setting; and to teach method without teaching subject matter. The exercises demand involvement sufficient to minimize the use of thought processes to disguise feelings.

Commonality Rather than Idiosyncrasy Is Emphasized

The class method allows a member to compare himself with others and observe those ways in which he is like others and those ways in which he differs.

Emphasis is on attitudes and values which are held in common or which are held by certain groups of people as opposed to other groups. The recognition of universal commonality of feelings serves to provide a relief from guilt and offer relief from the loneliness that is a common experience.

Communication Is Viewed as an Individual Responsibility

A person's own feelings must be the source and provide the content of his expressive communication. Each person's communication in the class is limited to that which concerns him. Each person is expected to refrain from assuming the responsibilities of others by communicating for them. No member is allowed to talk about the feelings of another member or interpret the feelings of others. No one is allowed to play the role of observer unless assigned to do so.

Claiming a generality, that is, avoiding individual responsibility by using the word "we" when talking about feelings, is not permitted. "I am not the only one who feels this way; a lot of others . . .," etc.

Whenever a participant is observed to be using a certain device to avoid his own communicative responsibilities, the leader arbitrarily rules against such an avoidance, whether it be in the act of communication itself or in the degree of involvement. The teaching methods employ explicit rules that most of the class will understand and aid in enforcing.

"You can only talk about yourself, not about others."

"You are not allowed to laugh when you are attacked. It is not funny."

"Do not give advice to others. Talk about your own feelings."

Discussion Is Limited to Communication with Intimate Peers

Communication with intimate peers, including spouses, close friends and adult relatives, presents the most serious problems. These problems not only can, but must, be solved if the person is to experience happiness and peace of mind. If sufficient emotional catharsis allows for the diminution of conflicts, the two people involved can find mutually satisfactory resolution of problems of increasing intimacy, difficulty and complexity. The lack of such catharsis and problem-solving procedures leads to estrangement in the relationship and increasing frustration and pain for the individuals involved.

Communicative problems with one's children are not considered appropriate subjects for discussion in the class sessions, since the discussion of relationships with other than adult peers is often used as a ploy to avoid communicative responsibility.

Likewise, employment problems are not acceptable for discussion in the class sessions. A participant can always allege—and perhaps rightly—that he will lose his job if he expresses his negative feelings to his employer; it is therefore fruitless to use such a relationship to exemplify communicative responsibility. Though, hopefully, a person will eventually be able to achieve a considerable measure of expressiveness in such complex areas as employment, as a beginning exercise in communication, power relationships are not appropriate.

Patients often conceive the doctor-patient relationship as a power relationship rather than a professional relationship and believe that since the doctor has the power to keep the patient in the hospital, the patient cannot afford to express his feelings for fear of reprisal. When a patient holds this view, it is valueless to employ discussion of a doctor-patient relationship to exemplify communicative responsibility.

Further, psychotherapeutic communication bears little relationship to the type of intimate peer communication selected as topics for these class sessions. In psychotherapy, the focus of interchange is entirely on the patient; it is the task of the therapist to facilitate the communication of the patient but not the task of the patient to facilitate the communication of the therapist. Moreover, the ultimate aim of psychotherapy is its own termination, while the ultimate aim of the intimate peer relationship is the continuation, extension, and deepening of the relationship.

Anonymity Is Not Allowed

Each person must acknowledge responsibility for his own communication by identifying himself with whatever he says or writes. All individual offerings are identified by name and cannot be cloaked in anonymity. Each class member is expected to "stand up and be counted" as one person.

The openness and sharing which the class exercises require is explained thoroughly, and members are cautioned against revealing anything they are unwilling for all others to know. A problem too personal for public venting should not be vented. Participants are not encouraged—much less forced—to reveal intimate problems; each individual decides entirely for himself just how much transparency he wishes to have.

Presence Is a Prerequisite to Participation

In whatever ways are possible, the leader stresses that interpersonal communication requires the physical and/or psychological presence of a person: absenteeism, whether physical or psychological, precludes communication. In the class, insistence upon physical presence is used to underscore the importance of psychological presence in a relationship. Therefore, persons absent during one period are not allowed to participate in the follow-up period. Late arrivals to class may not join already-formed groups but must serve as observers for the remainder of the class period.

Active Participation and Reciprocity Are Expected

Since the philosophy of the class calls for active participation in the processes of living, each exercise not only presumes total participation but in many situations makes it mandatory. Similarly, since reciprocity is an essential part of communication, a class participant must not only participate actively himself but must respond to the efforts of others.

Nonparticipation and Passivity Are Unacceptable

The leader attempts to levy a price for every nonparticipatory withdrawal or every passive response. The price for inactivity may be enforced nonparticipation, usually for one class period. A nonparticipating member may be asked to leave the class for the remainder of the period. When a member alleges that he likes to listen but not talk because he has "nothing worthwhile to say," he may be removed from the place where he can hear what others say, since no one else can hear him. Or his behavior may be labeled as "stingy," since he does not want to share with others. Every instance of passivity or lack of reciprocity is confronted directly with disapproval or with some unpleasant consequence.

Participants Are Expected to Follow Directions and to Do the Exercises as Presented

The instructor prescribes the channels of communication to be followed and gives explicit directions. Class members are expected to participate in the exercise as it is presented and to exhibit good will in their attempt to learn what is being taught. A persistent disinterest or unwillingness to participate in the exercises, as structured, results in disqualification for membership in the group. The leader is frankly autonomous as regards methodology.

Participants are asked and expected to follow the mode of communicative behavior which is for them the most difficult; the silent are expected to learn to talk, and the talkative are expected to learn to listen. The autistic participants are asked to give warmth and empathy, and the ingratiating, self-negating participants are asked for self-assertion.

The leader sets the situation, creates the atmosphere, and determines the class procedures. In each case, he selects the type of behavior to be rewarded, unrewarded, or perhaps even censured. Adaptive behavior receives approval; maladaptive behavior does not.

Concrete, Inanimate Objects Represent Abstract Concepts

Tangible symbols, without inherent value, represent ideas, feelings, concepts, or rewards for authentic responses. Slips of colored paper serve on one occasion to represent anger or guilt, or on another occasion to represent money. Strings become boundaries to enclose life space. Irregular pieces of paper, when labeled "moon rocks," are collected on a walk in inner space.

When participants communicate in the ways which are most difficult for them, they receive rewards that are tangible symbols of success. They receive an undesired symbol or fail to receive a symbol of success when they do not follow effective communicative procedures or when their lethargy prompts them to take "the easiest way out" of a problem.

A significant aspect of the technique is that the rewards are symbolic and materially worthless and useless. Such a technique is clearly appropriate for adults, who respond to identification of ideas in the simple, concrete terms.

Topics of Common Concern and Lay Vocabulary Are Used Throughout

The topics of the lessons have been derived from topics which have concerned human beings throughout history; from topics known to be especially troublesome to psychiatric patients; and from topics suggested by participants. Lay vocabulary is purposely employed instead of psychiatric terminology. Occasionally, a familiar psychiatric term, such as ambivalence, is explained in lay language.

Class or Group Recording Secretaries Are Frequently Used

A recording secretary for the class as a whole or for smaller groups has proved helpful in keeping notes on class experiences. Besides providing summaries for presentation the following period and serving as an aid in continuity, the recorder's notes provide bulletin board material at the end of each week. Recorder's notes have assisted in recapitulation of the materials for this book.

Homework May Be Assigned

Numerous devices may be used to bridge the gap between one class period and the next. Homework occasionally serves this end: participants receive a specific assignment to be accomplished before the next class meeting or they may be asked to bring to class a predetermined problem or some specific object for use in the class period.

A Bulletin Board Adds Color and Interest

A bulletin board, if available, stimulates further discussion among members and arouses interest in those who are not members of the class. Summaries of discussions and abstract representation of the ideas may be posted; maxims may be used as lead headlines. Members of the class can be involved in a variety of ways in the preparation of the bulletin board materials.

A Minimal Amount of Simple Equipment Is Needed

The appendix lists equipment useful in conducting the class sessions which are incorporated into this book. Each leader can, of course, select his own equipment and devise the most desirable methods of using it. In most cases, a variety of ordinarily available equipment could be utilized to accomplish or demonstrate the same points.

A chalkboard and movable chairs and tables are presumed in the basic setting. Without movable chairs or without tables, substantial adaptation of the lessons would be required.

Chapter III

METHODS SPECIFICALLY ADAPTED TO
THE TIMBERLAWN EXPERIMENTS

Though specific methods have been used in conducting the sessions at Timberlawn, numerous adaptations of the basic principles may be made to meet the unique needs of a specific setting. The following special adaptations in methodology were made for the Timberlawn setting.

An Open-Ended Group Was Inherent in the Situation

An open-ended group with a constantly shifting membership was inherent in the organization of the activities therapy program at Timberlawn Psychiatric Hospital. In an active, acute treatment center, newly admitted patients must be constantly scheduled into whatever activities are available. Therefore, almost every class meeting included participants new to the group and unacquainted with class procedures.

Adaptation to the open-ended group involved encapsulation of the lessons into reasonably succinct units, with a beginning and an ending. Each lesson is thus meaningful to some extent to one who has not been in the class previously. Likewise, the lessons provide a sense of completion to anyone discharged after a particular class meeting. To obtain maximum stability within the limitations inherent in the session, class sessions have been held three times a week, on consecutive days.

The open-ended group precludes the possibility of a logical or calibrated progression in difficulty, usually considered desirable in any teaching situation. Undoubtedly in many settings it would be possible to have a reasonably stable group for a considerably longer period of time.

***Physical Facilities Necessarily Limit the Class Enrollment,
but a Specific Class Size Is Not Requisite
to the Methodology***

The enrollment of the Timberlawn class has been consistently limited to 50, with approximately 35 in daily attendance. This size was arbitrarily arrived at because of the available classroom space.

The techniques have been chosen because of their applicability to more than the usual eight- to twelve-member therapy groups. Some of the techniques are suitable for use with much larger groups, since they incorporate "buzz session" microcosms of the larger group.

***The 50-Minute Class Hour, an Adaptation to the Schedule
Limitations, Is Not Inherent in the Methodology***

All classes in the activities program at Timberlawn have had the 50-minute hour limitation. Probably a 90-minute period would be ideal.

A Departmental Bulletin Board Is Used

The public nature of the class is made graphic by the use of a departmental bulletin board that exhibits individual contributions and summaries of classes for the scrutiny of other hospital patients as well as staff members and families who may be visitors to the hospital.

Chapter IV

BASIC CONCEPTS RELATED TO EMOTIONS

P OSSESSING EMOTIONS IS A universal human characteristic. Whenever one person interacts with another, even for a short duration of time, he becomes involved in experiences which produce emotion. Only when he chooses to talk about his feeling, however, are we able to know what his feeling is, when it arose, and what stimulated it, for feelings are never fully available to objective interpretation.

Though many types of emotions exist, most of them can be encompassed under the headings of love and hate, dependency, fear, shame and guilt, anger, and sexuality.

Emotions have many dimensions, the first of which we may refer to as degree. A small amount of anger, for example, we designate as annoyance. The largest amounts of anger are labeled rage, wrath, fury or outrage.

Another dimension is that which involves duration. Certain emotions such as rage are acute and short-lived, whereas others, such as hatred, are persistent and smouldering.

Some emotions are specifically directed toward the self and one's own behavior; remorse and shame are examples. On the other hand, behavior of others produces such responses as revulsion and humiliation.

Words may describe feelings a person has toward someone else—*protective* for example—or the responses one has to the ministrations of others in his behalf: *protected*.

A number of sequential factors, which will be subsequently amplified and explained, comprise an emotion.

The Emotogenic Stimulus Is Usually a Person

Feelings ordinarily represent responses to living people, usually present. Thus, the search for anger against *people* is more rewarding in insight than the search for anger against *things.*

Primitive man worshipped his environment. He peopled his world with good and evil gods who resided in external reality: fire, water, and the celestial bodies. Upon man rested the responsibility of propitiating these gods through offerings, in order that these temperamental gods would deign to meet his needs.

Modern man has theoretically supplanted his primitive animism with a monotheistic, less idolotrous type of religion; however, this relinquishment is actually superficial. All of us experience atavistic reversions to primitive animism, venting our anger on the recalcitrant ketchup bottle, the window that refuses to open, the faucet that stubbornly leaks, and the cake that simply will not rise, as if these objects were possessed with spite and perversity. In the news recently an item recounted an incident in which the proprietor of a gas station loaded his pistol and repeatedly shot the soft-drink machine which had persisted in stealing quarters from his customers. When charges were filed against the man, lawyers volunteered legal defense and money flowed in from similarly outraged empathizers.

To invest our environment with human qualities is to provide ourselves with a major form of defense: we can feel angry at *something* instead of *somebody.* Thus, we can avoid expression.

Feelings Are Not Subject to Control

A widely held misconception is that feelings are subject to control. In approaching problems related to feelings, most people believe their need is for greater control. "I have to learn to control my anger."

In truth, nothing is less subject to control than feelings. We are not aware of a feeling until we have experienced it, and the recognition of a feeling indicates its having already come into existence. Therefore, by the time feelings are recognized, they are no longer subject to control. They are. Once the stimulus has occurred, the feeling is automatic, autonomic. The question is not whether one will control the feeling or even whether or not he will express the feeling. The question is how, when, where, and in what way he will express the feeling, for express it he will. But since the human mind is extremely devious, it is often difficult, even impossible, to establish the connection between the feeling and the expression.

Emotions Consist of a Number of Phases

The Physiological Response

The human being's first response to a feeling is physiological. In human evolutionary development, emotions served a self-preservative function. When danger became imminent, the body prepared itself for fight or flight.

The physiological responses to a feeling are carried out by two systems: the voluntary system and the autonomic, or involuntary, nervous system. The voluntary system is concerned only with the stimulation of those muscles which can be consciously controlled, such as movements of arms or legs. The involuntary nervous system, as the name implies, functions automatically and supplies nerve fibers to many organs and blood vessels, providing stability or homeostasis for the body. Therefore, we find that the autonomic system is composed of two divisions, usually with opposing actions. For instance, a blood vessel may constrict or dilate, depending on the need at a given moment in a particular portion of the body. A common example of these opposing forces is blushing, which contrasts with pallor.

As specifically applied to feeling responses, voluntary muscle action may be controlled to a certain degree, but the stimulus which reaches the autonomic nervous system causes a variety of responses almost entirely out of our control.

The following are some of the numerous and various physiological systems of emotions: increased perspiration, excessive sweating of the palms of the hands and the soles of the feet, goose bumps, flushing of the face, giddiness, tremor, headache, dizziness, ringing in the ears, watering of the eyes, dry mouth and lips, crawling of the skin, upset stomach, diarrhea, frequency of urination, blurring vision, palpitations of the heart, shortness of breath, coughing, wheezing, chest pains, drowsiness, dullness, muteness, failure of memory, gurgling of the stomach, nausea, constriction of the throat and chest, insomnia, tenseness of neck muscles, generalized muscular tension, restlessness, and contortions of the facial muscles.

Awareness of the Feeling

Concurrently with the physiological response, we become aware of our feeling, sometimes in a generalized form, such as anger or fear. It is possible to develop not only an augmented awareness of feelings but the capacity to recognize feelings quicker and more definitively.

The Nonverbal Response

The next response to a feeling is a nonverbal response that is usually apparent to acute observers but may or may not agree with the verbal message. Nonverbal responses include laughing, smiling, frowning, hugging, kissing, patting, squeezing, hitting, clenching the fists, stamping the feet, nodding, raising the eyebrows, pursing the lips, clenching the teeth, biting the lips, narrowing the eyes, winking, etc.

With increased awareness, it becomes possible to inhibit, magnify, or distort the nonverbal responses shown. A "poker face" is a learned response. We can learn not to "wear the heart on the sleeve." We can gradually learn to keep many emotional responses hidden from all but our most intimate peers.

Examination or Denial

If the feeling reaches conscious awareness at all, hopefully the individual will avoid impulsive action and dwell with his feeling long enough to become fully aware of it and to subject it to examination, attempting to determine the source, the moment of onset, and the nature of the feeling.

If the person does not take the time to reach awareness, he may suppress, distort, alter, or misdirect feelings in an attempt to keep them out of consciousness, thus leading to self-deception and escalation of the disturbed emotions. When no attempt is made to understand the emotional process, the person proceeds directly to the action phase of his experience. Without self-examination and expression, he loses the values inherent in insight and catharsis and is subject to the painful consequences of impulsive and precipitous action.

The following interchange between a psychiatrist and a

patient illustrates the concept of "sitting with" feelings instead of either "sitting on" them or taking action.

Patient: "I'm so frightened, doctor, I just don't know what to do."

Psychiatrist: "Why do anything? Why don't you just be afraid?"[1]

Even a small amount of insight may produce a very large amount of change in a person's responses to recurring situations. A single moment of real insight can strip off a multitude of emotional complexities, revealing a nakedness that is somehow less frightening and less threatening than the self that is swaddled in defenses.

The more objective a person can become in his observation of his own feelings, the closer he comes to facts about himself. The more realistically he appraises himself, the greater potential he has for forsight and anticipation of his future behavior and ultimately for self-discipline. Objectivity can make it possible for him to plan self-constructive rather than self-destructive action and in so doing meet his own needs through his own behavior.

Verbal Expression

Verbal expression is of signal importance in revealing feelings for examination, serving as a bridge between unconsciousness and consciousness in feeling responses. Adequate verbal expression of feelings allows separation of action and emotion and may well obviate the need for any action at all.

Disturbing feelings, when properly understood and expressed, gradually atrophy or are neutralized. Thus, the same emotogenic stimulus may thereafter produce quite a different response or no significant response at all.

Once a decision is made to talk about feelings, it is possible to enlarge or limit the degree of verbal expressiveness and to alter the meaning and specificity of what is expressed. With considerable practice it becomes possible to postpone expression to a specific time and to decide what is appropriate to express in words and what can be more appropriately expressed in action.

---

[1] Patient interview by Thomas H. Allison, M.D., Timberlawn Psychiatric Hospital.

Behavior or Action

As a sequent to a feeling, action may or may not be taken. Action may be postponed, either temporarily or for a length of time. Action may be minimized, maximized, altered, or eliminated altogether.

Action may mean fight—either physical or psychological—or flight. Flight may mean literally running away or may be psychological—a social withdrawal that manifests itself in isolation, mutism, or pouting. Psychological withdrawal is commonly accomplished through drug addiction, alcoholism, apathy, or depression.

Action may consist of conscious choice and decision, more or less carefully planned, either individually or with one or more persons. Action may also consist of refraining from taking action; in fact, no action is one of the most important forms of action to be considered in any situation.

Action not in accord with society's values provokes negative responses from society and results in unpleasant consequences for the offender. For example, an individual invites unpleasant societal consequences upon himself by driving in a car while intoxicated. His jail sentence or fine makes evident the attitude of society toward his behavior.

Action frequently causes unpleasant or even tragic consequences for those not involved in taking the action. A person who drives while intoxicated may well maim or injure fatally someone wholly guiltless of the act.

Regardless of society's judgments, when an individual behaves in a manner unacceptable to himself, he suffers anger, guilt, remorse, regret, or other forms of psychic pain. One who desires freedom from psychic pain—peace of mind—must therefore learn to control his actions so that he lives within the bounds of behavior acceptable to his own conscience. Otherwise, his only alternative is to reeducate his conscience to accept his behavior. Either course is possible, but it is usually easier to modify behavior than conscience.

It is important to recognize the vast difference between feelings and deeds and to keep the two clearly separated. To think about doing something or to feel like doing something is not at all the same as doing it. Feeling is one thing. Action is another. Even though a person may believe that it is wrong to have *bad* feelings and that it is wrong to do *bad* things, the two are still not the same. *Bad* feelings may eventually be dispersed, but *bad* action is irrevocable.

Feelings may stimulate action, but feelings never justify action. Feelings do not absolve guilt related to action, and the feelings do not make the action right or wrong.

Desirably, all action should be self-generated and should be subject to the individual's control. The confidence that he can control his actions enables a person to liberate feelings and to behave spontaneously.

Imagining Feelings in the Future

Fortunately, and unfortunately, we are gifted with the ability to imagine. Actually experiencing a situation is not required in order to know what it must be like to face a situation. Having once experienced a feeling, an individual can imagine having similar feelings in the future. When uncontrolled and accompanied by little awareness or insight, imagining stress-filled situations and subsequent feelings is called "worry." When the imagination wholly replaces reality, it is called "delusion" or "hallucination."

The same agile imagination that produces mental illness also provides one of the major methods of remaining mentally healthy. The healthy person is able to produce and experience anxiety in anticipation of an event, in order to cope more efficiently with subsequent danger.[2]

Using imaginative foresight allows one to avoid experiencing emotions of frightening magnitude by avoiding situations which are needlessly emotogenic and to save his emotional stamina for handling situations which are unavoidable.

Through employment of the imagination, an individual can institute self-change in the least threatening situations, avoiding

---

[2] Jahoda, Marie: *Current Concepts of Positive Mental Health.* New York, Basic Books, 1958, pp. 42-43.

those in which his feelings would be too difficult to manage. Small problems can be attacked before they grow into really difficult ones. By weighing possible courses of action in the imagination, a person can learn to choose that action which will best satisfy his long-range needs as well as those of the present.

Consistent expression and planned action result in gradual dispersal of problems; recognized and attacked, problems fade away, releasing energy and time for the attack on new problems as they arise.

The concepts which have been amplified in Book II serve as a matrix of ideas from which the instructor may draw his responses to problems and ideas presented by the participants. These basic concepts should assist the instructor, as well as participants in the sessions and other readers of this book, to achieve the self-understanding and maturity the book has been designed to effectuate.

BIBLIOGRAPHY

Ardrey, Robert: *The Territorial Imperative*. New York, Atheneum, 1966.

Carroll, Lewis: *Alice in Wonderland*.

Clodd, Edward: *The Story of the Alphabet*. London, George Newnes, 1900.

Gralnick, Alexander (Ed.): *The Psychiatric Hospital as a Therapeutic Instrument*. New York, Brunner/Mazel, 1969.

Jahoda, Marie: *Current Concepts of Positive Mental Health*. New York, Basic Books, 1958.

James, William: *Psychology*. Cleveland, World, 1948.

Kling, Samuel G.: *Your Legal Advisor*. New York, Permabooks, 1955.

Kluckhohn, Clyde and Murray, Henry A. (Eds.): *Personality in Nature, Society and Culture*, 2nd. ed. New York, Knopf, 1953.

Lewin, Kurt: *A Dynamic Theory of Personality, Selected Papers of Kurt Lewin*. New York, McGraw, 1935.

Lewin, Kurt: *Resolving Social Conflicts*. New York, Harper, 1948.

Masteller, Kenneth C.: How to avoid financial tangles. *Economic Education Bulletin*, 7:1, 1967.

Menninger, Karl: *Love Against Hate*. New York, Harcourt, Brace, 1942.

Menninger, Karl A.: *Man Against Himself*. New York, Harcourt, Brace, 1938.

Pei, Mario: *Language for Everybody. What It Is and How to Master It*. New York, Pocket Books, 1958.

Rogers, Carl R.: Lecture: "My Way of Facilitating a Group." Fourth Annual Institute for Psychiatric Education, Dallas, Dallas League of Nurses and Timberlawn Foundation, March 30, 1969.

Ross, Martin J.: *Handbook of Everyday Law*. New York, Harper, 1959.

Ruesch, Jurgen and Bateson, Gregory: *Communication: The Social Matrix of Psychiatry*. New York, Norton, 1951.

Starch, Daniel: *How to Develop Your Executive Ability*, 7th ed. New York, Harper, 1943.

Wells, Evelyn: *What to Name the Baby*. Garden City, Garden City Books, 1953.

RECOMMENDED READING LIST

Berne, Eric: *Games People Play: The Psychology of Human Relationships.* New York, Grove, 1964.

Bugental, J. F. T.: *The Search for Authenticity.* New York, Holt, Rinehart and Winston, 1965.

Cumming, John and Elaine: *Ego and Milieu: The Theory and Practice of Environmental Therapy.* New York, Atherton, 1966.

Ellis, Albert and Harper, Robert A.: *A Guide to Rational Living,* 1970 ed. North Hollywood, Wilshire, 1970.

Fromm, Erich: *The Art of Loving.* New York, Harper, 1956.

Fromm, Erich: *Escape from Freedom.* New York, Avon, 1965.

Glasser, William: *Reality Therapy: A New Approach to Psychiatry.* New York, Harper and Row, 1965.

Hall, Edward T.: *The Hidden Dimension.* Garden City, Doubleday, 1966.

Hall, Edward T.: *The Silent Language.* Garden City, Doubleday, 1959.

Hayakawa, S. I.: *Language in Thought and Action,* 2nd ed. New York, Harcourt, Brace, 1964.

Huizinga, John: *Homo Ludens: A Study of the Play Element in Culture.* Boston, Beacon Press, 1950.

Jourard, Sidney M.: *The Transparent Self.* Princeton, Van Nostrand, 1964.

Malamud, Daniel I., and Machover, Solomon: *Toward Self-Understanding: Group Techniques in Self-Confrontation.* Springfield, Thomas, 1965.

Maslow, Abraham H.: *Toward a Psychology of Being,* 2nd ed. New York, Van N-Rein, 1968.

Masserman, Jules H.: *Modern Therapy of Personality Disorders.* Dubuque, Wm. C. Brown, 1966.

Masserman, Jules H.: *The Practice of Dynamic Psychiatry.* Philadelphia, Saunders, 1955.

Menninger, Karl, Mayman, Martin, and Pruyser, Paul: *The Vital Balance.* New York, Viking Press, 1963.

Offer, Daniel, and Sabshin, Melvin: *Normality: Theoretical and Clinical Concepts of Mental Health.* New York, Basic Books, 1966.

Oversteet, Bonaro W.: *Understanding Fear in Ourselves and Others.* New York, Collier, 1962.

Overstreet, H. A.: *The Mature Mind.* New York, Norton, 1949.

NOTE: All of the theoretical books listed in the bibliography have proved meaningful as background reading material for the sessions. In addition, this list is recommended for further elaboration of theory.

300

Rogers, Carl R.: *Client-Centered Therapy*. Boston, Houghton-Mifflin, 1951.

Rogers, Carl R.: *On Becoming a Person: A Therapist's View of Psychotherapy*. Boston, Houghton-Mifflin, 1961.

Rogers, Carl R.: *Becoming a Person: Two Lectures Delivered on the Nellie Heldt Lecture Fund*. Austin, Hogg Foundation for Mental Health, 1956.

Ruesch, Jurgen: *Disturbed Communication*. New York, Norton, 1957.

Schutz, William C.: *Joy: Expanding Human Awareness*. New York, Grove, 1967.

Szasz, Hans: *The Myth of Mental Illness*. New York, Harper, 1961.

EQUIPMENT NEEDED

Bulletin board
Chalkboard
Dictionaries
Easel
Hole puncher
Mimeograph machine
Paper cutter
Record player

SUPPLIES

Balls of various sizes and weights
Beans, preferably larger sizes, a pound or more as needed
Blankets, felt or carpeting for table covers
Box, dress size
Brads, 3 in.
Cards picturing the sign language of the deaf
Chalk
Cloth strips 2 in. wide and 3 ft. long or clothesline in pieces
   3 ft. long
Commitment Contract, one for each participant
Construction paper, assorted colors
Dowel sticks, 3/8 in. or 1/2 in. in diameter and 9 in. long
Envelopes
Erasers
Gummed paper tape, 3 in. wide
Hood, large enough to fit over the head and having slits for the
   eyes
Legal document covers
Manila tag board, 12 x 18 in. and 24 x 36 in.
Notary Seals, gold (Denison, No. 32-321 (4521))
Origami paper for folding
Penny

Pens, felt-tipped or china-marking crayons
Paper, 8½ x 11 in. and 8½ x 14 in.
Paper, lined
Paper, graph
Pencils
Play money
Records, Capitol 2015, Glen Campbell, *By the Time I Get to Phoenix*
Records, dance (walk tempo)
Records (march tempo)
Rubber cement
Sack, large enough to cover a human being
Scissors
Scratch board
Sign, *Notary Public*
Signs, 0% and 100%
Stencils
String (large ball)
Tape, masking
Tape, transparent
Tiddly Winks, a number of sets
Timing device (stop watch or kitchen timer)
Warranty Deed to Feelings, one for each participant
Yardsticks

INDEX

A

Absence, of communication, 30-32
Acceptance, the, 253, 255, 261, 265
Accident proneness, 162
Accidents, 162
Accomplishment, sense of, 103, 232
Acknowledgment
  of differences, 192, 194, 195
  of good will, 193, 194, 195
  of receipt of message, 8
Action, 294-297
  altering of others', 280
  anticipation of feelings before, 218
  avoidance of, 90-91
  commitment to one, 67
  discussion to precede, 218
  impulsive, 169-170
  inciting to, 171-172
  parentally approved, 79
  postponement of impulsive, 54, 167
  repetitive, 163, 217
  selection of the, 243-244
  selecting composite, 198-199
  self-exhortation to avoid, 88-91
Activities therapy, viii
Adolescence, the task of, 84
Affirmation, 241, 274
Aggression, 183, 243-245
Alienation, 278
Allison, Thomas H., 295
Alternatives, 68, 69, 200, 202, 206, 209
Ambivalence, 54, 60, 61, 67, 68, 69, 91
  commitment to act despite, 282
American Board of Psychiatry and
    Neurology, viii
Anger, 125
  produced by gifts, 153
  self-defense and, 176
  self-directed, 130
  tightrope between guilt and, 208

B

Balsam, 17
Bateson, Gregory, 17, 278
Baylor University, School of Nursing,
    viii
Beans, 143
Bi-polar thinking, avoidance of, 218
Bloss, Charles L., 129
Boundaries of self, 176
Burton, Sir Richard Frances, 78

Anonymity, not allowed, 285
  see also Names
Annoyance, 48-51
Anxiety and unexpressed emotions, 280
Animism, 292
Apple, halving the, 204-207
Ardrey, Robert, 110, 112
Astronauts, 73-74
Asylum, lunatic, 62
Attack, 176, 179, 182
  and initiative, 176
  more potent if planned, 177
Authenticity, 176
Authority figures, 78, 84

C

Campbell, Glen, 53
Carelessness, 162
Carroll, Lewis, 232
Catharsis, 7, 52, 244, 279, 284, 294
Chemotherapy, vii
Cheshire cat, 232
Choice, 67, 85-87, 202-207, 239-242
  avoidance of, 149
Class length, 290
Class size, 290
Clodd, Edward, 7, 27-28

305

S

Sack, 30-32
Sakade, Florence, 95
Self, 182
  boundaries of, 176
Self-actualization, 176
Self-assertion, 110
  constructive, 183
  demanded of participants, 286
  vigorous, 244
Self-awareness, ix
Self-change, xi, 272, 297-298
Self-confidence, 232, 280-281
Self-correction, 280, 281
Self-crucifixion, 164
Self-deception, 39-40, 294
Self-defense, constructive, 183
Self-definition, lack of, 281
Self-delineation, 126
Self-effacement, a device for hostility, 97
Self-esteem, 219, 241-242, 274
  a concommitant of participation, 280-281
Self-exhortation, 88-89
Self-exploration, 73
Self-interest, language of, 7
Self-knowledge, 7, 217
  through comparison, 135
Self-love, 281
Self-messages, 84-85
Self-revelation
  caution against, 285
  devices to induce, 144-145
  voluntary, xii
Shakespeare, William, 150, 241
Singularity, 103-108
Small talk, 54
Social Work, viii
Solutions, multi-faceted, 218
Southwestern Medical School of the University of Texas, viii
Spending and saving, 128
Spontaneity in taking action, 199
Starch, Daniel, 204
Subjectivity, 52
Supplies, list of, 302, 303
Swift, Jonathan, 67

Symbol, 20, 21, 132, 287
Syrus, Publilius, 67

T

Tension, 173
Territorial imperative, 110
Terror, frontispiece
Thanatos, 243
Therapeutic community, vii
Therapeutic intervention, vii
Timberlawn Foundation, 227
Timberlawn Psychiatric Hospital, viii, xi, 157
  specific methodology for, 289
Time, prime, 241
Timing, factor in problem solving, 198
Transparency, 140-142
  voluntary, 285
Trespass, 177
Trust, 62

U

Undercommitment, 248-252
Understanding, providing data for, 278

V

Verbal messages, 20
Verbal communication
  criteria for effective, 52
  lack of, a hazard, 174
Vigor, bodily, 21
Violence, 171, 177
Voice, small still, 79

W

Warranty Deed to Feelings, 231
Wells, Evelyn, 132, 133
Words
  substitutes for
    aggressiveness, 279
    destructiveness, 279
Worry, 297
Writing, 7, 20, 27-28